Consequences of Small-Farm Mechanization

INTERNATIONAL RICE RESEARCH INSTITUTE AND
AGRICULTURAL DEVELOPMENT COUNCIL

1983
INTERNATIONAL RICE RESEARCH INSTITUTE
Los Baños, Laguna, Philippines
P.O. Box 933, Manila, Philippines

FOREWORD

MECHANIZATION OF SMALL FARMS in South and Southeast Asia affects all production stages from land preparation through crop production, harvesting, and postharvest processing. Because adoption of agricultural machinery increases capital input, it is expected that either the level of output should increase or the level of other inputs decrease. Such changes are likely to have an impact on employment, income and income distribution, and social welfare.

Evaluation of the consequences of mechanization as well as formulation of appropriate policy guidelines is a predominantly empirical issue strongly related to local socioeconomic conditions. The most frequently used analytical approach is a detailed study of a relatively specific situation.

In 1977, the United States Agency for International Development (USAID) agreed to fund a research project — The Consequences of Small Farm Mechanization on Production, Income, and Rural Employment in Selected Countries of Asia — undertaken jointly by the International Rice Research Institute (IRRI) and the Agricultural Development Council Inc. (A/D/C). The project has involved collaborative work with national research institutions in Indonesia and Thailand, as well as smaller projects with individual researchers in many countries.

A series of planning and monitoring workshops was held at IRRI to review project progress. The fourth workshop, in which study results from both A/D/C and IRRI were presented, was held 14-18 September 1981. A summary report of the papers and discussion is available upon request from the IRRI Agricultural Engineering Department.

A committee comprising Dr. K. Adulavidhaya, Dr. H. P. Binswanger, Mr. J. B. Duff, Mr. J. Lingard, Dr. R. Sinaga, Dr. J. P. G. Webster, and Dr. J. A. Wicks reviewed the papers presented and selected those for inclusion in this book. The committee recommended that three papers on farm mechanization in Pakistan be consolidated into a single paper (second chapter). It also recommended that 12 papers for the Philippines, West Java, and South Sulawesi studies be summarized in the final three chapters.

The work of all who prepared papers for the workshop is gratefully acknowledged. Dr. J. A. Wicks undertook the technical editing of the papers, assisted for specific papers by Mr. J. Lingard, Dr. G. Nelson, and Dr. J. P. G. Webster. G. P. Hettel, assisted by G. S. Argosino, edited the final papers.

This book should provide useful information on the consequences of mechanization, and we hope it will stimulate further research.

M. S. Swaminathan
Director General
International Rice Research Institute

The International Rice Research Institute (IRRI) was established in 1960 by the Ford and Rockefeller Foundations with the help and approval of the Government of the Philippines. Today IRRI is one of 13 nonprofit international research and training centers supported by the Consultative Group for International Agricultural Research (CGIAR). The CGIAR is sponsored by the Food and Agriculture Organization (FAO) of the United Nations, the International Bank for Reconstruction and Development (World Bank), and the United Nations Development Programme (UNDP). The CGIAR consists of 50 donor countries, international and regional organizations, and private foundations.

IRRI receives support, through the CGIAR, from a number of donors including:

the Asian Development Bank
the European Economic Community
the Ford Foundation
the International Fund for Agricultural Development
the OPEC Special Fund
the Rockefeller Foundation
the United Nations Development Programme

and the international aid agencies of the following governments:

Australia
Belgium
Brazil
Canada
Denmark
Fed. Rep. Germany
India
Japan
Mexico
Netherlands
New Zealand
Philippines
Spain
Sweden
Switzerland
United Kingdom
United States

The responsibility for this publication rests with the International Rice Research Institute.

ISBN 971-104-082-4

Contents

Foreword

Mechanization of rice production in developing Asian countries: perspective, evidence, and issues   **1**
R. W. HERDT

Farm mechanization in Pakistan: policy and practice   **15**
B. LOCKWOOD, M. MUNIR, K. A. HUSSAIN, and J. GARDEZI

Innovation in the Philippine agricultural machinery industry   **31**
K. W. MIKKELSEN, and N. N. LANGAM

Economic analysis of the farm machinery industry and tractor contractor business in Thailand   **39**
S. WATTANUCHARIYA

Productivity growth of the agricultural machinery industry in Thailand   **51**
P. WIBOONCHUTIKULA

Domestic resource cost of agricultural mechanization in Thailand: a case study of small rice farms in Supanburi   **61**
S. SUKHAROMANA

Causes and consequences of power tiller utilization in two areas of Bangladesh   **71**
M. A. JABBAR, M. S. R. BHUIYAN, and A. K. M. BARI

Economic, technical, and social aspects of tractor operation and use in South Sulawesi, Indonesia   **85**
J. HAFSAH and R. H. BERNSTEN

Economics of pump irrigation in Eastern Nepal   **95**
M. R. KHOJU

Effect of tubewells on income and employment: a case study in three villages in Kediri, East Java, Indonesia   **107**
T. SUDARYANTO

Comparative analysis of thresher adoption and use in Thailand and the Philippines   **119**
F. JUAREZ and R. PATHNOPAS

Labor use patterns and mechanization of rice postharvest processing in Bangladesh   **139**
J. U. AHMED

Consequences of small rice farm mechanization in the Philippines: a summary of preliminary analyses   **151**
A. M. AGUILAR, E. C. CAMACHO, A. C. GENERALLA, P. B. MORAN, J. F. SISON, Y. TAN, and J. A. WICKS

Consequences of small rice farm mechanization in West Java: a summary of preliminary analyses   **165**
Y. SAEFUDIN, H. SISWOSUMARTO, R. BERNSTEN, A. SRI BAGYO, J. LINGARD, and J. WICKS

Consequences of small rice farm mechanization in South Sulawesi: a summary of preliminary analyses   **177**
Y. MAAMUM, I. G. P. SARASUTHA, J. HAFSAH, R. BERNSTEN, R. SINAGA, and J. WICKS

MECHANIZATION OF RICE PRODUCTION IN DEVELOPING ASIAN COUNTRIES: PERSPECTIVE, EVIDENCE, AND ISSUES

R. W. Herdt

A generalized sequence of mechanization of Asian rice production is developed, based on experience in Japan, Taiwan, and Korea. By 1978, these countries had reached a relatively high level of mechanized riceland preparation. Labor force growth rates among Asian countries are compared. A net social benefit model for evaluating the desirability of mechanizing rice production is outlined and often neglected factors are identified. Available empirical evidence on some important factors is reviewed and the question of who benefits from mechanization is addressed.

There is considerable controversy about the desirability of agricultural mechanization in Asia. One extreme view equates mechanization with modernization so that it becomes the major indicator and requirement for development. In the late 1970s, modernization in agriculture in the People's Republic of China was synonymous with mechanization. Those who point out the psychological benefits from riding a tractor rather than walking behind a carabao have similar ideas in mind.

A more moderate view holds that the functional relationship between power input and agricultural output is analogous to that between fertilizer and yield, so that development requires added power in the form of mechanization (Hamid 1979). Binswanger (1978) refers to this as the net contribution view.

A third view holds that the major objective is absorbing the significantly increasing numbers of laborers in the agricultural sector during the next 20 years, and that mechanization can help through intensifying land use (Southworth 1974). In this view, mechanization is the key to increased cropping intensity which will permit labor absorption at other times during the production cycle. A major benefit of mechanization then is the increased agricultural output generated from larger harvested area and higher yields resulting from deeper plowing and better cultivation practices.

The International Rice Research Institute.

A fourth view, somewhat different from the first three, opposes agricultural mechanization on the grounds that it is a straightforward substitution of capital for labor and, given the labor supply in most Asian countries, is socially undesirable (Abercrombie 1975). In some cases, this is supplemented with the idea that distortions in the price ratio of labor to capital have been a primary factor responsible for speeding mechanization, and that nonmarket forces have been largely responsible for these distortions.

The purpose of this paper is:
- to provide a perspective on the issues through an examination of historical experience in East Asia; and
- to provide a framework for criteria to judge the impact of machinery introduction and other technological changes.

One additional note: mechanization means different things in different situations. Our discussion deals with powered equipment, mostly two-wheel tractors (power tillers) and power threshers.

PATTERN OF MECHANIZATION IN ASIAN RICE PRODUCTION

Economic, technical, and policy factors are important in determining the pattern and speed with which rice production is mechanized in a country. Alternative investment opportunities and the prices of land, labor and capital influence demand for farm machinery. The perceived social opportunity costs of these resources influence policies which restrain or encourage mechanization, and the relative abundance of resources influences their private and social costs. Technical factors which influence engineering feasibility and the relative cost of mechanization include the amount of power required for a given task, the degree of judgment needed to apply the power, and the question of whether the task requires moving through the field. Climatic or soil conditions may also influence the relative difficulty of designing successful machines.

A generalized sequence of mechanization
Because every country in Asia has different technical and economic conditions, it is unlikely that identical patterns of mechanization will take place. However, the broad similarities in relative factor abundance and the tasks required for wet-rice cultivation indicate a general pattern of rice mechanization is likely to emerge. To date, among the Asian rice economies, only Japan has fully mechanized production. Following the Japanese pattern, Taiwan and Korea are well started and a number of other Asian countries are moving in the same direction.

In East Asia, investment in land improvements and water control preceded mechanization. This was partly an accident of history. Improved water control was carried out using human and draft animal power, and was one of the few ways to improve the productivity of agricultural land in the high man:land economies. Most of Japan's rice fields were supplied with irrigation facilities by the 19th century, and the major subsequent improvement was investment in drainage, providing a high degree of water control (Ishikawa 1981). The same water control investment occurred later in Korea and Taiwan, where there were "many years of rural infrastructure creation" prior to 1940 (Fei and Ranis 1975). Most of this took the form of gravity irrigation and drainage but, with the availability of electricity and internal combustion engines, power pumps have become one of the first machinery investments for many rice producers. In areas of South and Southeast Asia, where gravity systems are inadequate to permit efficient water control and ground water resources are available, investment in private pumps has been substantial (Patel and Patel 1971). Electric irrigation pumps replaced foot-operated pumps in Japan during the 1920s, long before power tillers were used (Ishikawa 1981). A 1966 study in an intensive rice double-cropping area of Taiwan noted that 1 water pump was available for every 3 farms while there was only 1 power tiller for every 18 farms (Lai 1972).

In addition to pumps, other investments in land were important prerequisites for successful mechanization in East Asia. Drainage to provide a hard enough soil base for machines, enlargement of plots and consolidation of fragments, and construction of farm roads to reach individual plots were important in some areas (Tsuchiya 1972).

The introduction of land preparation equipment and threshers followed development of a high quality land base. Small manual threshers were among the first widely adopted mechanical devices (Lee 1972).

They were later introduced into a number of other countries by the Chinese and Japanese, but never became established. Power threshers however, were widely adopted in both East Asia and some areas of other countries. In Japan, two-wheel power tillers were introduced in the early 1950s. Land preparation was the first operation mechanized in parts of the Philippines and Thailand. Tillers may initially be very small as in the case of the 2- to 3-hp "iron cow" introduced in Taiwan (C. K. H. Wu 1972), but after some years machines in the 8- to 12-hp range seem to take over.

It seems to be more difficult to develop appropriate machines for other rice production tasks such as planting, fertilizing, cultivating, and drying. These operations present formidable technical problems. Weeding, for example, requires considerable judgment and relatively little power. Some mechanical weeders have been developed, but herbicides have proven to be cheaper and more effective at distinguishing weeds from rice. Transplanting has been mechanized, but requires special techniques for raising seedlings and is still quite labor intensive. Despite these problems, the Japanese had developed commercial machines for each major operation by the late 1970s.

There are substantial divergences from this path. Four-wheel tractors of 35-60 hp have been introduced into Thailand, Malaysia, the Philippines, and Pakistan. In some areas, these units are rented for initial land preparation, and draft cattle used for secondary land preparation. Old and new technologies coexist. The large tractors have, in some cases, preceded a high degree of water control development as in central Luzon or central Thailand where their presence in sugarcane farming may have stimulated adaption to rice. In other cases, government authorities (such as the Muda River Development Authority of Malaysia) own the tractors and rent them to farmers.

Data to measure the degree of, and forces contributing to, mechanization are somewhat fragmentary. The FAO publish data on wheel and crawler tractors, garden tractors, and a few other kinds of machinery, but there are many gaps in the series for Asian countries. Definitions are unclear and may be inconsistent from country to country. Time series data on the number of power tillers and farm wage rates are available for Japan, Taiwan, and Korea for a number of years, although the wage rates for Taiwan are incomplete. The data provide some clues to the importance of certain forces in the mechanization process.

A supply and demand model provides an oversimplified, but still useful,view. Rice production machinery can be supplied either by imports or from domestic production. Imports are generally under government limitation or licensing. Domestic production may occur through private initiative, but experience in Japan and Taiwan shows that concessional government credit, subsidies, tax exemptions, and government efforts have been major forces speeding the development of appropriate rice production machinery (Kudo 1972, T. C. Wu 1972).

Machinery supply from the private sector is a function of the development stage of the industrial sector and the alternative earning opportunities for industrial capacity. The latter is related to the scale of investment needed to begin production of farm machinery compared to other industrial products. Potential earnings of export industries may make governments willing to set policies encouraging or discouraging mechanization. Government investment in farm machinery research and development is an obvious encouragement, while taxation and import restrictions are barriers. Of course, there are limitations in the extent to which governments will subsidize imported machinery or invest in machinery research and development. So, the supply of agricultural machinery is determined by market forces in the industrial sector, together with the decisions of government to tax or subsidize imported machinery.

The demand for rice production machinery is determined by the degree to which it substitutes for labor or other inputs, the price of labor relative to substitutes, and the price of rice. Machinery well adapted to the technical requirements of a particular agricultural setting will be more productive and substitute for a greater value of alternative inputs. A high price for rice increases the demand for machinery.

The data in Table 1 are broadly consistent with the preceding static equilibrium concepts, although many other forces within each country affect the mechanization level. They show that Japan is the most highly mechanized country of the region. In the early 1970s, it had 6 power tillers for every 10 ha of cropland and 5 tractors for every 100 ha. Farm wage rates approached $10/day and the price of rice was the highest anywhere in the world. Taiwan and Korea had wage rates about four times as high as any other country except Japan and were well started toward the adoption of power tillers. Korea had the second highest rice price with Taiwan not far behind. Several countries had a small number of tractors, but these were used for road transportation, plantation and other nonrice crops (Sri Lanka and Malaysia), or on a contract basis for initial land preparation for rice (Malaysia, Philippines, Thailand). Power tillers had been introduced in small numbers to many countries, but except for Thailand and the Philippines, they were still available in strictly experimental numbers. Wage rates and rice prices in most South and Southeast Asian countries, with the possible exception of Malaysia, were far below those in the East Asian

Table 1. Power tiller and tractor numbers, wage rates, and rice prices in Asia, 1971-75 average.[a]

	Tillers (no./1000 ha cropland)	Wheel, crawler tractors (no./1000 ha)	Farm wage rate		Farm price of rough rice (US$/t)
			US$/day	kg rough rice/day	
South Asia					
India	[b]	1.0	0.26	2.1	125
Pakistan	+[c]	1.6	0.39	3.3	119
Sri Lanka	0.1	6.1	0.42	2.6	161
Bangladesh	+	0.3	0.68	3.3	206
Southeast Asia					
Malaysia	0.4	2.3	2.53[d]	12.9[d]	195
Thailand	8.0[d]	1.1	0.59	7.9	75
Philippines	4.1[d]	1.0	0.34	3.1	109
Indonesia	+	0.5	0.71[d]	4.3[d]	167[d]
Burma	0.1	0.8	0.39	7.0	56
East Asia					
Japan	615	48.5	8.78	15.6	563
Taiwan	38	0.6	2.80	17.1	164
Korea	20	0.1	2.07	9.3	223
China	130[e]	7.5	n.a.	n.a.	n.a.

[a]Sources: Tiller numbers from the IRRI Agricultural Engineering Department. Tractor numbers from FAO Production Yearbooks, but tiller numbers in Thailand and China are from Ishikawa (1981). Wage rates and rice prices from *World rice statistics* (IRRI). World price averaged $310/t of rice equal to about $200/t of rice over the period 1971-75. Data for China from personal communication from Hua Guozhu, vice director, Chinese Academy of Agricultural Mechanization Sciences. [b]No data available, but the author estimates there are less than 0.5/1,000 ha. [c]No statistical estimates available; the author estimates less than 0.05/1,000 ha. [d]Refers to 1976. [e]Refers to 1978.

countries. So it appears that rice production in most of South and Southeast Asia was not poised for rapid mechanization. However, even though Japan was so far ahead of the other Asian countries, examining mechanization there may still be relevant for the rest of Asia.

Japan's experience
In 1950, agriculture in Japan was just entering the early stages of mechanization with many small pedal threshers, some 13,000 power tillers, and an equal number of power sprayers, but essentially no other machinery. The industrial sector, recovering from World War II, was beginning to pull increasing numbers of workers from rural areas. Thirty years later more than 4 million power tillers were being used, and rice production, from transplanting to harvesting, was essentially mechanized.

In 1950, Japan had about 2 power tillers/1,000 ha of cropland. Early data on threshers are not available, but in 1955 there was 1 thresher/3 ha. By 1960, there was 1 tiller/12 ha and 1 thresher/2.5 ha. During the 1960s, the size and capacity of Japanese tillers increased and the riding tiller was introduced. By 1970, there was 1 tiller/1.7 ha, apparently more than adequate. Thereafter, the number of ordinary walking tillers remained constant while there was a rapid increase in the number of riding tillers. The 1970s also saw the rapid introduction of powered rice transplanting machines and combine harvesters, and more power sprayers and dusters. There were also significant numbers of power reapers and reaper-binders during the 1960s although data are fragmentary.

During the same period, there was a sharp decline in the agricultural labor force and a steady reduction in the hours of labor per hectare in rice production (Ishikawa 1981) as machines were substituted for human labor. Some observers clearly saw the trend toward mechanization as a drive to achieve economic efficiency, pushed by rising labor costs, rather than as a continuation of the earlier Japanese drive to increase yields. Tsuchiya (1972) claimed that "mechanization has been advanced in order to secure a certain amount of rice at the lowest possible cost, rather than to increase the yield."

Differences within East Asia

Korea and Taiwan are the only Asian rice producing countries other than Japan to have achieved any significant level of mechanization by 1980. The pattern of power tiller introduction in the three countries is in Figure 1.

In 1960, Taiwan had as many tillers per 1,000 ha as Japan had in 1950, but the number increased more slowly. After 10 years, Taiwan still had only about 2 tillers/100 ha. However, by 1977, 20 years after the initial introduction, there was nearly 1 tiller/10 ha, and by the 1980s nearly all of Taiwan's riceland was prepared by machines. Power tillers were introduced into Korea's rice sector about a decade after introduction in Taiwan, and their rapid adoption was similar to that in Japan, reaching 7 tillers/100 ha in about 10 years, with continued rapid increases thereafter.

Four critical points in the mechanization process are identified in Table 2: 1) the

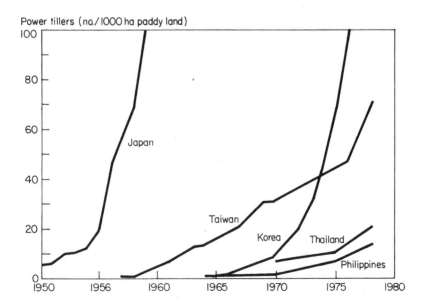

1. Power tillers in 5 Asian countries, 1950-80.

Table 2. Farm-level rice prices and wage rates during comparable periods of agricultural mechanization in Japan, Korea, and Taiwan.

| State of mechanization | Tillers (no./1000 ha) | Period | Prices (US$) | | | Real wage (kg paddy/day) |
			Rice/t	Wages/ day	World rice	
Japan						
Initial	Introduction	pre-1950	na	na	na	na
Early	2.5	1950-51	311	0.70	na	3.4
Takeoff	20	1956	328	1.00	134	4.7
Full	100	1961	327	1.47	137	6.9
Korea						
Initial	Introduction	1961	173	0.85	154	7.2
Early	2.5	1968	216	1.36	201	9.6
Takeoff	20	1972	338	2.02	148	9.2
Full	100	1978	559	5.99	367	16.5
Taiwan						
Initial	Introduction	1955-56	86	na	134	na
Early	2.5	1961[a]	98	0.88	137	9.7
Takeoff	20	1970	176	1.77	143	10.1
Full	100	1978	376	7.06	367	27.9

[a]Taiwan passed 2.5 tillers/1,000 ha in 1958, but wage data are not available for that year. 1961 is the first year they are available. [b]Taiwan had 70 tillers/1,000 ha in 1978, the year for which data are shown. By 1979 or 1980, it had undoubtedly passed 100 tillers/1,000 ha.

initial stage; 2) the early stage with about 2.5 tillers/1,000 ha, a conspicuous number of tillers with an insignificant proportion of the land served; 3) the takeoff stage with about 20 tillers/1,000 ha, about 20% of the land served; and 4) full mechanization with about 100 tillers/1,000 ha, enough to (theoretically) serve the entire rice area. The data for East Asia show great differences in real agricultural wage measured in rice equivalent at mechanization takeoff. At the takeoff stage, a day of labor cost about 5 kg of rice in Japan, about 9 kg in Korea, and about 10 kg in Taiwan. These differences suggest that farm-level demand for machinery may have been very different in the three countries. However, wage rates converted into kilograms of rice reflect the domestic price of rice as well as of labor. All three countries, indeed all Asian countries, insulate their rice prices from the world market, thereby distorting them in one direction or the other.

In contrast, the industrial sectors of the three countries have been well aligned to opportunities in the international market. So, it can be argued that the cost of mechanization reflected the world market and the price of rice reflected policy views on how to achieve the desired pace of development. In Japan in the early 1950s, both labor and rice were so valuable as potential foreign exchange earners that there was a strong drive to mechanize. In addition, institutional factors, such as restraints on land sales and consolidation to larger units, encouraged the development of part-time farming which could only conveniently be done with machinery. Korea has followed a similar path, but with an even higher price of rice, encouraging rapid mechanization in the 1970s. Taiwan, in contrast, has had a low rice price and has maintained more labor on the farm through rural industrialization policies, and thus retarded mechanization.

DESIRABILITY OF MECHANIZING RICE PRODUCTION

The East Asian countries mechanized when labor used in rice production became sufficiently valuable in alternative industrial employment that it could no longer be used in the rice sector. The data in Table 1 indicate that only Malaysia, Thailand, and Burma have ratios of agricultural wages to rice prices that approach those in the East Asian countries, but that the low value of rice in Thailand and Burma makes wages appear high. It appears that Malaysia may be the next country to adopt rice mechanization.

Labor force growth rates
Knowing the growth rate of the nonagricultural labor force, the total labor force, and agriculture's current share, one may calculate the growth rate of the agricultural labor force needed to absorb the available labor in an economy (Mellor 1966). This process can be understood by examining the following relationship.

$$x = (1 - a) Z + a Y \tag{1}$$

where:
  x is growth rate in the labor force as a whole,
  Z is growth rate of the agricultural labor force,
  Y is growth rate of the nonagricultural labor force, and
  a is proportion of the labor force in the nonagricultural sector.

This relationship states that the growth rate in the total labor force is the weighted average of the growth rates of the labor force in the two sectors of the economy. Given this, one can easily determine the growth rates, needed in the two sectors to achieve certain objectives. For example, one can calculate the growth rate in nonagricultural employment required to absorb all new entrants to the labor force. Conversely, one can determine how fast the agricultural labor force will grow, given certain initial conditions, by rewriting equation 1 as:

$$Z = (x - aY)/(1 - a) \tag{2}$$

So, for a country with 25% of the labor force in the nonagricultural sector, an 8% growth rate in the nonagricultural labor force, and a 3% growth rate in the total labor force, the relationship yields 1.33% $(3 - 0.25(8)/0.75)$, while a country with the same proportion in the nonagricultural sector and the same overall growth in total labor force, but only 5% growth in the nonagricultural sector, yields 2.33%.

Typical values for important Asian rice-growing countries are in Table 3. The growth rate of the labor force in the nonagricultural sector is not readily available, so we use the growth in urban population. This, if anything, overstates the growth rate of the nonagricultural labor force and understates the growth rate of the agricultural labor force. Among the Asian countries, only Korea, Taiwan, and Japan have reached the stage of declining agricultural labor forces. Burma had a temporary decline in the early 1970s because of very low rice prices and earlier slow population growth. This will change over the next 2 decades with the rise in the growth rate of the total labor force. All the other countries have added to their agricultural labor force at 1%/year or more during the 1970s and will continue to add 1-2%/year

Table 3. Growth rates of total labor force (L. F.) and nonagricultural portion, and resulting residual rate of growth in agricultural L. F., Asian countries, 1970-2000.[a]

	Growth rate of labor force		Growth rate of nonagricultural L.F.[a,b] 1970-75	% of L.F. not in agricultural 1977	Resulting calculated growth in agricultural L. F.	
	1970-77	1977-2000			1970-75	1977-2000
Thailand	2.5	2.3	3.5	23	2.20	1.94
Pakistan	2.4	2.8	4.1	42	1.17	1.86
Philippines	2.1	2.6	3.5	49	0.75	1.74
Bangladesh	2.3	2.7	6.3	22	1.17	1.68
Burma	1.4	1.9	3.8	45	-0.56	1.46
India	1.7	1.9	3.1	27	1.18	1.46
Indonesia	2.0	1.9	3.3	40	1.13	0.97
Sri Lanka	2.1	2.2	3.7	46	0.74	0.92
Malaysia	3.6	3.0	4.8	56	2.07	0.71
Korea	2.9	1.9	5.4	55	-0.16	-2.38
Taiwan	1.9	1.6	4.4	66	-2.95	-3.84
Japan	1.3	0.8	2.4	86	-5.46	-9.03

[a]Calculated from data in IBRD, World Development Project Report, 1979. [b]Growth rate in urban population used as proxy.

during the next 20 years. The main rice producing countries of Asia have had, and will continue to have, increasing numbers of people available for rice production.

Social benefit:cost framework

Given the increasing supply of agricultural labor, questions must be raised about the desirability of introducing machines that replace labor. The argument that farm machinery may provide the key input necessary to overcome a labor bottleneck is persuasive, but should be reflected in economic benefits. For economies struggling with development problems, mechanization can only be justified if it generates benefits for society — regardless of the psychological benefits of seeing tractors in one's field. What are the benefits and costs of mechanization and how are those costs and benefits shared within society? The net social benefit (NSB) of mechanization, equal to agricultural output valued at shadow prices less agricultural inputs valued at shadow prices, can be stated as:

$$NSB = Q_r P_r^* + Q_n P_n^* - L_r P_l^* - K_r P_k^* - T_r P_t^* - L_n P_l^* - K_n P_k^* - T_n P_t^* \qquad (3)$$

where the subscripts r, n, l, k, and t refer to rice, other crops, labor, capital, and land, respectively; Q's refer to output quantities produced; L, K, and T refer to the input quantities of labor, capital, and land, respectively; and P^*s are shadow prices.

Output can be further defined as the product of area harvested times average yield, while area harvested equals geographic area times cropping intensity. Defining C_r, the rice cropping intensity, as total area of rice harvested divided by geographic crop area and C_n, the other cropping intensity, as total area of other crops harvested divided by geographic crop area gives

$$Q_r = C_r A Y_r \qquad (4)$$

and $\quad Q_n = C_n A Y_n \qquad (5)$

where A is the geographic crop area and Y_r and Y_n are the yields per harvested hectare of rice and other crops.

Substituting equations 4 and 5 for 3 gives:

$$NSB = C_r A Y_r P_r^* + C_n A Y_n P_n^* - L_r P_l^* - K_r P_k^*$$
$$- T_r P_t^* - L_n P_l^* - K_n P_k^* - T_n P_t^* \tag{6}$$

The impact of any particular change, such as that generated by mechanization, can be expressed as the total differential of equation 6:

$$dNSB = A Y_r P_r^* + dC_r + C_r A P_r^* dY_r + C_r A Y_r dP_r^* + A Y_n P_n^* dC_n$$
$$+ C_n A P_n^* dY_n + C_n A Y_n dP_n^* - P_l^* dL_r - L_r dP_l^* - P_k^* dK_r - K_r dP_k^*$$
$$- P_t^* dT_r - T_r dP_t^* - P_l^* dL_n - L_n dP_l^* - P_k^* dK_n - K_n dP_k^*$$
$$- P_t^* dT_n - T_n dP_t^* \tag{7}$$

Some components of equation 7 are expected to change dramatically with mechanization. These are the focus of most investigations on the impact of mechanization. Other components are commonly assumed to be constant while still others are generally ignored. A brief review may be useful.

P_r^*, P_n^* : The prices of rice and other crops are generally assumed to be invariant with the techniques of production although, if output effects of changes in technique are large, they may change.

Y_r, C_r, Y_n, C_n : The production of rice and other crops may change as a result of changing yield and changing land use intensity.

A : The geographic crop area is generally assumed to be fixed because there is little new land to be exploited except in a few remote areas.

P_l^*, P_k^*, P_t^* : The shadow prices of labor, capital, and land are generally considered to be invariant with respect to changes in production techniques. This assumption may be valid only in the short run where the rice production sector is small relative to total use of each input.

$P_i^* = P_i + D_i$: The shadow prices of inputs equal their market prices, P_i, plus a difference which may be recognized as a distortion factor, D_i.

L_r, K_r, T_r : The use of inputs in rice production is a major factor usually assumed to change with technical innovation.

L_n, K_n, T_n : The use of inputs in production of other crops may also change with a change of technology, but these are usually ignored.

Because many of the factors that may change have been ignored in the empirical work on the impact of mechanization, it is impossible to draw any firm conclusions although investigations to date provide some indications as to the size of certain impacts.

A second dimension of the impact of mechanization is the distribution of NSB among earners in the production process. Relatively little on this issue is available in the empirical literature, aside from the obvious statement that, in a market-directed economy, laborers receive the returns to labor and farmers, or capitalists, receive the returns to capital. All consuming groups would obtain some portion of the benefits to increased output via its impact on the market price of rice.

Empirical studies have been cast in a much narrower framework than just suggested and so it is impossible to evaluate from them the NSB of any change. However, a necessary (but not sufficient) condition for society to benefit from the change is that *either*

- the total output value of crops produced be increased with no change in value of inputs; or
- machinery be introduced where the social cost of labor is rising relative to the social cost of capital.

In either case, the identified change will have a positive impact on NSB, which will be reflected in a lower social cost of rice production. This lower social cost of output, if transmitted through the market, will result in lower rice prices. If neither condition holds, then it is unlikely that there is any NSB from mechanization.

NSB, as used in this discussion, has only an efficiency implication. Equity or overall social desirability is not inferred by either its increase or decrease. A situation, leading to an increase in NSB with a decrease in equity or a decrease in NSB with an increase in equity, may be selected because society decides it is worthwhile to trade off some equity for the efficiency obtained. It seems evident, however, that society would never knowingly choose a situation that leads to a decrease in NSB *and* a decrease in equity. Given the existing price distortions (taxes, tariffs, subsidies, imperfect competition) in most developing economies, it is likely that use of market prices to evaluate benefits may produce an erroneous conclusion of a given change leading to increased efficiency. The importance of using shadow prices cannot be overstressed when evaluating NSB.

A general equilibrium framework

Although the formulation of NSB in the preceding section takes account of the impact on rice and other crops, it is a single-sector, partial-equilibrium model because it does not account for changes that may occur in the nonagricultural sector of the economy. That requires a whole economy or general equilibrium approach. If rice production uses domestically manufactured machinery, rice production mechanization may generate considerable income and employment in the machinery sector. The amount will vary with the labor intensity of machinery production. The increased income generated from manufacturing machines will generate an increased demand for rice. If that increased income is concentrated in economic classes with a high income elasticity of demand for rice, the feedback impact on the rice sector will be larger than if the increased income went to classes with a low income elasticity of demand.

These interrelationships can be measured in an input-output (I-O) model of the type developed by Leontief (1951). I-O models define economy as a whole in which all inputs used in the production of each commodity are identified and measured. Manipulation of these models can lead to insights on the impact the changes in one sector can have on other sectors. I-O analysis has the advantage of quantifying both the direct employment impact of machines substituting for labor in rice production, as well as the indirect impact of the increased labor used in producing, distributing, and servicing these machines. Such models can be developed by building on existing I-O models which planning ministries have already developed for most countries.

WHO GAINS FROM MECHANIZATION

If mechanization results in increased output, it will tend to push prices down and the benefits will be shared by rice consumers, whether they be landless agricultural workers, farmers, or urban people (Hayami and Herdt 1977). The absolute benefits to various individuals are positively related to the proportion of their incomes spent on rice consumption.

In the absence of increased output, machinery adoption may shift earnings from one group to another. That is, a machine which replaces labor will receive the wage formerly paid to the laborers. In such an event, the machine owner receives the earnings formerly paid to laborers. There is an inherent difference in the ownership pattern of capital and labor. In the absence of slavery, labor can only be owned at a rate of 1 unit/person, or at most 5-10 units/household. On the other hand, ownership of capital can be and, in most economies, is concentrated in the hands of relatively few, usually through inheritance, political power, or business acumen. Concentrated capital ownership means that income earned by capital also is concentrated. The introduction of machinery has redistributing effects which, when it also leads to increased output, will add to the welfare of low income rice consumers and technology adopters. When machinery has no output effect, it simply redistributes income.

Farmers will have an incentive to adopt machines when the machines reduce production costs. However, if reduced costs are achieved through subsidies on the purchase price or through low cost credit, then farmers are responding to artificial (policy-induced) market prices that diverge from the real, or shadow prices. If machine use results in a faster output growth rate, policymakers must evaluate the trade-off between more output and income redistribution from labor to capital. But if there is no output effect, the decision to promote mechanization supports a transfer of income from labor to machinery owners, without an offsetting benefit.

The extent to which landless agricultural workers depend on earnings from hired farm employment varies widely. Under many conditions, they are highly dependent on agriculture, and perhaps even more dependent on the earnings obtained during the harvesting season. Clearly, the actual impact of any reduction in the demand for labor depends on the proportion of their incomes deriving from operations which become mechanized and the alternative employment opportunities. Because that varies, careful assessment of the likely impact of mechanization is very important.

REFERENCES CITED

Abercrombie, M. 1975. Agricultural mechanization and employment in developing countries. *In* Effects of farm mechanization on production and employment. FAO, Rome.

Binswanger, H. P. 1978. The economics of tractors in South Asia. Agricultural Development Council and ICRISAT.

Fei, J. C. H. and G. Ranis. 1975. Agriculture in two types of open economies. *In* L. Reynolds, ed. Agriculture in development theory. Yale University Press, New Haven.

Hamid, J. 1979. Agricultural mechanization: a case for fractional technology. *In* Tan Bock Thiam and Shao-er Ong, eds. Readings in Asian farm management. University of Singapore Press, Singapore.

Hayami, Y. and R. W. Herdt. 1977. Market price effects of technological change on income distribution on semisubsistence agriculture. Am. J. Agric. Econ. 59(2):245-56.

Ishikawa, S. 1981. Essays on technology, employment and institutions in economic development. Econ. Res. Ser. 19. Institute of Economic Research, Hitotsubashi University, Tokyo, Kinokuniya Company, Ltd.

Kudo, Z. 1972. Implications of farm management research for government mechanization programs. *In* H. Southworth, ed. Farm mechanization in East Asia. Agricultural Development Council, New York.

Lai, W. C. 1972. Current problems of farm management on mechanized farms. *In* H. Southworth, ed. Farm mechanization in East Asia. Agricultural Development Council, New York.

Lee, C. C. 1972. Economic and engineering aspects of mechanization of rice harvesting in Korea. *In* H. Southworth, ed. Farm mechanization in East Asia Agricultural Development Council, New York.

Leontief, W. W. 1951. The structure of American economy, 1919-39. 2nd ed. Oxford University Press, New York.

Mellor, J. W. 1966. The economics of agricultural development. Cornell U. Press, Ithaca, New York.

Patel, S. M., and K. U. Patel. 1971. Economics of tubewell irrigation. Indian Institute of Management, Ahmedabad.

Southworth, H. M. 1974. Some dilemmas of agricultural mechanization. *In* H. Southworth and M. Barnett, ed. Experience in farm mechanization in Southeast Asia. Agricultural Development Council, New York.

Tsuchiya, K. 1972. Mechanization and relations between farm, non-farm and government sectors. *In* H. Southworth, ed. Farm mechanization in East Asia. Agricultural Development Council, New York.

Wu, C. K. H. 1972. Analysis of machinery-labor relationship in farm mechanization. *In* H. Southworth, ed. Farm mechanization in East Asia. Agricultural Development Council, New York.

Wu, T. C. 1972. Government policies promoting farm mechanization. *In* H. Southworth, ed. Farm mechanization in East Asia. Agricultural Development Council, New York.

FARM MECHANIZATION IN PAKISTAN: POLICY AND PRACTICE

B. Lockwood, M. Munir, K. A. Hussain,
and J. Gardezi

The first part of this report contains reviews of the government of
Pakistan's farm mechanization policy from 1975 to the present,
and of a 1975 World Bank study questioning the suitability of
rapid introduction of tractors. The study concluded that although
farmers with tractors had good returns on their mechanized
investments, these private gains were at the expense of substantial
social advances for rural society. The second part presents some
results of an A/D/C-funded study of farm mechanization in Punjab Province conducted in 1978-79. Data on the behavioral pattern
of farms with a tractor generally supported the findings of the
World Bank study particularly in terms of the transfer of farmland
from tenants to farmers with tractors and the loss of jobs and
earnings for the rural landless community.

COUNTRY SITUATION AND FARM MECHANIZATION POLICY

Agriculture is the largest sector in the Pakistan economy and 75% of the population
live in rural areas. Fifty-three percent of the work force is employed in agriculture,
which produces about 30% of the GNP and accounts for about 36% of foreign
exchange earnings from merchandise exports. Large parts of the industrial and
service sectors depend on raw materials and customers from the agricultural sector.

The agricultural sector consists of some 5 million farms with an average area of
4 ha, a highly skewed distribution, and a high incidence of tenancy. About 70% of
the 19.3 million ha of cultivated farmland are irrigated, mainly from a large network
of canals which provide water to 74% of the irrigated area. The late 1960s to the early
1970s was a period of rapid agricultural change. There were improvements in the
availability and control of water through an expansion of canal capacity and
considerable farmer investment in tube wells, increasingly greater supplies of chemical fertilizer, and the rapid adoption of high yielding wheat and rice varieties. These
changes led to more intensive farm operations and land use, greater farm income,
and increasing demand for more and better farm power.

The Agricultural Development Council, Inc., and University of Agriculture, Faisalabad.

In 1965, animals constituted the main source of farm power — there were about 10.5 million work animals and only about 10,000 tractors. Between 1966 and 1970, 18,000 tractors, mainly in the 36 to 55-hp range, were imported, but there remained an increasing government concern that agriculture was being adversely affected by a power shortage, and that mechanization was the answer.

The main set of guidelines governing farm mechanization policy in Pakistan was drawn up in a major government study between 1968 and 1970 (Farm Mechanization Committee 1969, 1970). The committee estimated that tractors supplied only 14% of available farm power in 1978 and that work animals still dominated the scene with 75%. Total available farm power was estimated to be about 0.04 hp/ha of cultivated farmland; a suggested minimum requirement was 0.08 hp/ha.

The Farm Mechanization Committee proposed a tractor import program (Table 1) and the popularization of tractor-powered implements. The 1968 survey had shown that, while most tractor owners owned cultivators, very few owned moldboard and disk plows for primary tillage, or row planters, seed drills, fertilizer distributors, wheat threshers, and combines. The tractor import program was expected to increase total farm power availability from 0.04 in 1968 to 0.068 hp/ha in 1985. The share supplied by animal power would decline from 75 to 35%, the contribution of human power would fall from 11 to 6%, and the share provided by tractors would rise from 14 to 59%. In absolute terms, the committee predicted a decline in work animals from 3.65 to 3.26 million hp, a small increase in human labor from 0.53 to 0.55 million hp, and a substantial increase in tractors from 0.66 to 5.46 million hp.

This program was the crux of the committee's report and is the basis of Pakistan's farm mechanization policy to the present. The committee also made recommendations on a wide range of related aspects of farm mechanization. These included agricultural conditions, socioeconomic aspects of farm mechanization, standardization, manufacturing, spare parts, repairs and servicing, prices of agricultural machinery (including duties and taxes), the system and financing of imports, credit, technical manpower requirements, facilities for education and training, and research and extension.

The committee recognized that tractors were going predominantly to large farms, and that there was a tendency for large-tractor farms to grow even larger through resumption of land previously farmed by tenants. The ex-tenants, however, were

Table 1. Farm Mechanization Committee's proposed tractor imports program.

Time	Tractors (no.)				
	At beginning of plan period	Replacement needs	Net addition	Total import/ manufacture	Progressive total at the end of plan period
1969	17,100	500	4,000	4,500	21,100
1971-75	25,000	12,200	23,600	35,800	48,600
1976-80	48,600	24,200	32,700	56,900	81,300
1981-85	81,300	46,100	41,100	87,200	122,400

being absorbed as farm labor and the tractors on such farms were serving as a supplemental power source, not necessarily as tenant replacements. The small farmers were self-cultivators and the introduction of tractors did not create any tenant displacement problems (Farm Mechanization Committee 1970).

All machines are imported since Pakistan has not developed the capacity to manufacture tractors. Tractor introduction began slowly, and until 1957 there were no restrictions on makes and models. Consequently, there were at least 30 different makes or models operating and owners were experiencing maintenance and spare parts problems. In 1978, the government restricted future imports to seven makes, then continued to control and standardize the range of tractors available. While this policy made sense, it had a checkered history as the government depended increasingly on credit and barter trade arrangements for the supply of tractors and changed the range of acceptable makes accordingly.

Between 1965 and 1969, the World Bank, through provision of International Development Association (IDA) credits totaling $43 million, was a major financer of the farm tractor program. By 1970, the Bank had become concerned about possible adverse effects and initiated a study to examine "the major consequences of the introduction of large scale tractor technology in Pakistan." The report (McInerney and Donaldson 1975) was based on a survey of 202 farmers who had purchased tractors through the first IDA credit, mainly in 1967. The main findings were:

- the average size of the farms grew by a factor of 2.4,
- the average number of crops cultivated increased from 4.77 to 7.30 per farm and cropping intensity increased from 111.5% to 119%,
- the areas sown to fodder crops decreased by 50% with land transferred mainly to wheat and rice,
- labor use per farm increased but labor use per cultivated hectare declined by 40%,
- taking into account displacement of tenants each tractor replaced 8-12 full-time jobs,
- tractor use averaged about 1,200 hours/year,
- the private rate of return on investment was 57%,
- the social rate of return was 24%, and
- significant social costs resulted from adjustments in the pattern of resource use.

Two major policy questions arose 1) why did farmers adopt such a behavioral pattern, and 2) how can it be reversed. McInerney and Donaldson (1975) broadly discussed the kind of policies which could increase social benefits and reduce social costs. They also questioned the appropriateness of the basic unit of the mechanization program: a 10- to 30-hp tractor could spread the private benefits more widely among the rural population and incur lower social costs.

The land reform legislation of 1972 and 1977 put ceilings on land ownership and attempted to improve the security of tenants, but landowners were adept at getting around the legislation and the tenant position worsened. There is no evidence that the land reform legislation did anything to curb the predatory behavior of the tractor-farms, and the land accumulation activities of farmers who have acquired tractors have continued unchecked.

Government farm mechanization policy was not affected by high social costs. It continues to be based on the power shortage argument of the Farm Mechanization Committee and implementation involves little more than the importing of tractors and provision of cheap credit to tractor buyers. The policy is stated in the Fifth Five-Year Development Plan 1978-83 as 1) the "liberal import of tractors, sold at market price without subsidy;" 2) improved availability of tractors through their "assembly and progressive manufacture" in Pakistan; and 3) "allowing the importation of 2-year-old second-hand tractors and power tillers . . . freely against genuine foreign exchange earnings/savings of Pakistanis working abroad" (Planning Commission 1978).

The main question is not "whether tractors" but "how many tractors." An import program was recommended by the Farm Mechanization Committee for 1971 to 1985. In 1975, a FAO Mission was commissioned to review the program for the Fifth Development Plan and recommended that 15,000 tractors should be imported in each of 1976 and 1977 to catch up with "demand," and that during the plan period, annual imports should be between 10,000 and 11,000. When the plan came out, it specified that "about 15,000 tractors will be imported annually . . . to wipe out, *inter alia*, the backlog demand. The net population of tractors, excluding replacement is expected to go up from about 71,000 in 1977-78 to 111,000 in 1982-83" (Planning Commission 1978). On 16 August 1981, the Federal Agriculture and Food Minister announced that the government had decided to import 20,000 tractors annually.

Average annual imports from 1965-66 to 1974-75 were 4,040 units, mainly in the 36- to 55-hp range, but between 1975-76 and 1980-81 average annual imports stood at 14,470, with a shift to the 47- to 66-hp range.

Other aspects of the mechanization policy, for example, assembly and manufacture of tractors, power tillers, and implements, have not been implemented as vigorously. The Agricultural Development Bank of Pakistan (ADBP) has played the leading role in providing cheap credit (12%) for purchasing tractors and tubewells. It has consistently provided loans on about half the new tractors purchased each year, covering about 90% of the purchase costs. A disproportionately high percentage of these loans have gone to large (influential) farmers. To counter this, ADBP and the Rural Supply Cooperative Corporation initiated in 1979, a special scheme to lend up to 50% of the cost of a tractor to Punjab farmers with 5-10 ha. In 1979, 784 tractors were financed under this scheme (13% of all tractor loans). Also in 1979, ADBP started making loans for purchasing wheat threshers. Until then, the bank had kept away from financing tractor-powered farm implements.

THE A/D/C FARM MECHANIZATION STUDY

During 1978-79 A/D/C supported three projects on farm mechanization in Pakistan to investigate:
1. farmers' decision making for investment in farm machinery, with special reference to tractors;
2. the capacity of workshops and farmers to repair and maintain farm machinery; and
3. the effect of the adoption of mechanical wheat threshing on rural labor.

Study procedure
The team conducted three surveys during 1978-79, two involving farmers and one involving tractor repair/maintenance workshops, spare parts shops, and implement manufacturers.

Data obtained in the first farm study covered factors affecting farmers' decision making, their capacity to service and maintain tractors, details of tractor use in own-farm and hire service activities, and historical information on farm mechanization. This last requirement was the main influence on the survey design. Faisalabad District was selected as the survey area and a random sample of 40 villages was drawn from the district subdivisions. The villages were stratified so that half were on main roads and half on minor roads. A presurvey visit identified 125 farmers owning 129 tractors. Villages with fewer than two tractors were excluded. Four farms were operated by managers for absentee owners and the managers did not feel free to cooperate; three were owned by nonfarmers and 19 farmers could not be contacted during the survey and two subsequent visits. The survey was conducted in 25 villages with 88 tractor-owning farmers.

The sampling method facilitated collection of historical data. It caused problems in assessing the consequences of mechanization on the size of farms, tenants, cropping patterns, and land use intensities. Because we were dealing with farmers who had owned tractors between a few months and 25 years, recall data would have been stretching the memories of some respondents. In analyzing the "before and after" data relating to the major consequences of introducing tractors (farm area, tenants), we compromised by excluding farmers who purchased tractors before 1973.

The thresher study was conducted near Multan, an area where wheat is the major winter season crop and cotton the major monsoon-summer crop. Four villages were selected — two in a fairly standard farm area and two in a river-flats area of predominantly large farms. In each village, random samples of 15 farmers each were drawn from mechanical wheat thresher owners and those who threshed their 1978-79 wheat crop by traditional methods. A problem was that very few large and medium farmers were still threshing by bullock. Most were contracting mechanical threshing of their wheat. Therefore, the average wheat area for farms threshing mechanically (by farmers who owned threshers) was 19.4 ha; that for farms threshing with bullocks, only 2.8 ha. This prevented comparing farms which differed only (or even mainly) in threshing method.

Farm mechanization in Faisalabad District
Most farmers in areas with usable underground water began mechanization with diesel or electric tubewells. The tubewell often preceded the purchase of a tractor and cultivator by several years. Seventeen respondents only began active farming when they bought their first tractor; before this they had leased out their farmland. Generally, tractor investment committed the farmer first to mechanized land preparation and to other operations such as threshing later. The pace of farm mechanization accelerated after 1973 (Table 2). All farmers bought their first tractor and cultivator simultaneously. Investment in other tractor attachments before 1973 was fairly uncommon but then increased rapidly.

Table 2. Farm machinery purchased by 88 sample farmers.

	Farm machinery purchased (no.)								Tractor farms
	Tubewell	Tractor and cultivator[a]	Trailer	Wheat thresher	Pulley	Leveler	Cane crusher	Other items[b]	
To 1965	16	5	–	–	–	–	–	1	3
1966	5	2	1	–	–	–	–	–	5
1967	1	2	–	–	–	–	–	1	6
1968	7	3	1	–	–	2	1	1	9
1969	–	6	–	–	–	–	–	–	13
1970	5	3	4	–	1	4	1	–	15
1971	1	5	1	2	4	2	–	–	20
1972	1	3	1	2	3	–	–	–	22
Subtotal	36	29	8	4	8	8	2	3	
1973	3	8	2	2	–	–	–	3	29
1974	4	13	3	1	3	8	–	1	40
1975	2	12	8	8	9	7	2	1	50
1976	7	18	9	4	6	2	2	–	65
1977	3	19	16	11	15	12	1	2	80
1978[c]	5	13	13	23	18	7	2	–	88
Subtotal	24	83	51	49	51	36	7	7	
Total	60	112[d]	59	53	59	44	9	10	
% of farmer owners in 1978	50	100	63	58	63	46	10	5	

[a] Usually purchased together. [b] Seed drill (5), rototiller (3), disk harrow (2). [c] To August 1978 only. [d] Although 112 tractors had been purchased, 22 had been sold. The 90 tractors were operating on the sample farms in 1978.

Table 3. Expected benefits from tractor ownership.

| Expected benefit | Responses from 88 sample farmers | | | |
	First priority	Second priority	Third priority	Total
More farm income	36	22	8	66
Timely farm operations	10	8	3	21
Self-cultivation (removing tenants)	16	4	–	20
Income from hire services	5	10	1	16
Easier farming	8	3	1	12
Saving bullock expenses	4	6	2	12
Overcoming labor shortage	3	5	4	12
Others	5	2	2	9

The sequence of events culminating in tractor purchase usually began with leasing tractor services for land preparation, cartin, or threshing. In our sample, 96% of 72 tractor farmers who had operated farms prior to buying a tractor had been leasing for 4 to 5 years before purchase. Expectations varied, but clearly, many anticipated increased farm income from more timely operations, capability to manage larger farms (ejection of tenants), and off-farm income from offering tractor services (Table 3). Interestingly, the sons of 30 farmers demanded a tractor before agreeing to stay on the farm.

Generally, farmers had little or no choice as they had to purchase, make and model available when their bank loans were approved, or other funds were in hand. So, ownership pattern is not a good guide to farmers' preferences. In most cases, however, farmers replaced tractors with units of higher horsepower: the trend was from 44- to 45-hp to 46- to 48-hp units and, in many cases, 55- to 65-hp units. Most farmers preferred a particular make and model and matched it and work task with considerable consistency: Ford 4000 (55 hp) for heavy duty general work, Fiat 640 (64 hp) for long periods in the summer heat driving a wheat thresher, Bylarus (55 hp) for heavy hauling of bricks, and the Massey Ferguson 135 (47 hp) for general cultivation work.

The average cost of a tractor increased from $1,800 to $5,810 between 1968 and 1978 and, while the ADBP loans rose, many farmers had to find increasingly large sums from other sources. After 1973, credit from sellers of secondhand tractors and other noninstitutional loans became important, particularly for small farm tractor buyers.

Table 4. Sources of funds for tractor purchases by 88 sample farmers.

| Operational farm size in 1978 (ha) | Farms (no.) | Percentage of purchase cost | | | | | |
| | | Cash | | | Loan | | |
		Overseas remittances	Farm income	Other income	Bank	Private	Seller
Less than 10	23	24	17	14	34	1	11
19-19.5	31	11	17	7	52	9	4
20-39.5	23	2	52	2	4	3	0
40 & above	11	0	19	0	78	3	0
Total	88	10	23	6	49	6	5

Based on average cost figures (1973-78) for the different items, the package investment in a tractor and implements cost about $8,900 — tractor ($5,650), cultivator ($320), thresher and pulley ($1,770), and trailer ($1,140). The total investment in farm machinery by the sample farms was about $680,000, of which 48% had come from the farmers' resources, 31% from bank loans, 7% from overseas remittances, and 10% from other sources. Bank loans were restricted almost completely to tractor investments, and were biased toward larger farmers (Table 4). Smaller farms relied more on overseas earnings because they bought a number of secondhand tractors on credit from sellers and noninstitutional sources. Tractor attachments were mainly financed from farmers' funds.

Consequences of tractorization

Although there were considerable differences in time and methods, between the current survey and McInerney and Donaldson, the results are remarkably similar.

Changes in farm size. Only the 62 farmers who bought their first tractor after 1972 were included in this assessment. Changes between the year before tractor purchase and the end of 1978 are in Table 5. The first group increased their farm size by either reducing the farmland rented out to tenants (70%) or increasing the area rented in (30%). Forty-five tenants lost their farms, possibly more if the area rented in by the tractor-farmer was previously tenanted. Landlords, who became operating farmers only when they bought tractors, accounted for 17% of the total farm area in 1978. Thirty percent of their 1978 farm area was rented in and 70% was land previously rented out. Thirty-three tenants lost their farms as their landlords became farmers.

Our survey, made almost 10 years after McInerney and Donaldson's, should remove some doubts about the causal relationship between farm size expansion and tractor ownership, although not about the direction of the relationship. The resumption of tenanted land argues for the tractor as a final facilitating factor, while the increase in farmland rented in shows the tractor initiated the farm size expansion. In Table 6, classifying farmers into pretractor farm size categories shows that the "predatory behavior" of a large proportion (59%) was not restricted to those beginning as large farmers. The Farm Mechanization Committee had claimed that small farmers behaved differently. In our sample, 82% of the pretractor farmers were

Table 5. Changes in operated farm area, before and after tractor purchase, by direction of change.

Change	Farmers (no.)	Area farmed before tractor (ha)	Area farmed in 1978 (ha)	Proportional change
Increased the farm area operated	24	279	532	1.91
Did not change the farm area operated	22	274	274	1.00
Decreased the farm area operated	3	56	36	0.64
Began farming	13	0	171	—
Did not farm	1	0	0	—
Total or av	62	609	1,013	1.66

Table 6. Changes in average operated farm area and sources of change before and after tractor purchase, by pretractor farm size.[a]

Pretractor operated farm (ha)	Farms (no.)	Operated farm (ha)		Rented in (ha)		Rented out (ha)		Tenants (no.)		Proportional change		
		Before	After	Before	After	Before	After	Before	After	Operated farm	Rented in	Rented out
Less than 10	16	5.6	8.8	0.5	1.6	3.0	0.3	0.8	0.2	1.58	3.00	0.11
10-19.5	24	12.2	18.1	1.1	3.2	4.6	0.4	1.1	0.1	1.48	2.96	0.09
20-39.5	8	23.2	28.1	3.2	5.2	6.6	1.9	1.9	0.4	1.21	1.64	0.29
40 and above	1	40.5	40.5	10.1	10.1	–	–	–	–	1.00	1.00	–
All farms	49	12.4	17.2	1.5	3.1	4.3	0.6	1.1	0.2	1.38	2.10	0.14
Nonfarmers before tractor	14	0	12.3	0.7	5.1	8.5	0.6	1.9	0.2	–	6.94	0.07

[a]Farmers who purchased tractors 1973-78.

Table 7. Changes in average operated farm area and sources of change before and after tractor, by year of tractor acquisition.[a]

Year of tractor purchase	Farms (no.)	Operated farm (ha)		Rented in (ha)		Rented out (ha)		Tenants (no.)		Proportional change		
		Before	After	Before	After	Before	After	Before	After	Operated farm	Rented in	Rented out
1978	7	10.4	14.4	1.8	1.9	3.4	0	0.9	0	1.39	1.04	–
1977	11	11.2	16.4	0.4	1.6	6.2	1.9	2.0	0.5	1.47	4.33	0.31
1976	12	10.7	12.3	2.2	3.8	1.4	0.1	0.4	0.1	1.15	1.73	0.09
1975	5	15.1	25.3	2.9	7.0	8.1	0	1.4	0	1.67	2.39	–
1974	9	15.2	21.1	1.3	2.4	5.6	0.8	1.2	0.3	1.39	1.79	0.14
1973	5	14.4	19.1	0	3.2	1.4	0	0.4	0	1.33	–	–
All farms	49	12.4	17.2	1.5	3.1	4.3	0.6	1.1	0.2	1.38	2.10	0.14

[a]Only farmers who acquired their tractor 1973-78 and who had previously farmed.

"small" by the committee's reckoning (up to 20 ha), but they expanded their farms by a factor of 2.51 and expelled 33 tenants. The 14 pretractor landlords were also fairly small landowners: the average holding was 8.5 ha, and only one owned more than 20 ha. The smallest landlord (0.5 ha) expelled his single tenant and rented in another 6 ha. It is clear that expelling tenants and renting in additional land are not restricted to any one group.

We agree with the conclusion of McInerney and Donaldson that "the tractor is a powerful force narrowing the spread of farm sizes by pulling up the lower end of the size distribution." These practices do not appear to be declining (Table 7).

Changes in land use. Although one of the dominant arguments for mechanization is that it should lead to significant increases in cropping intensity, McInerney and Donaldson found an increase of only 8%. In our survey, the overall result was even more dismal — an increase of 4-5%. However, there was considerable variation in cropping intensity changes when farms were categorized by initial size (Table 8). The increase was also greater on farms without tubewells by a factor of 1.20. This suggests that the tubewell farmers had already increased cropping intensity as a result of better water supply and control, and that this, more than the tractor, influenced cropping intensity. However, as in McInerney and Donaldson's study land for farm enlargement may have been appropriated from small farms which might have had a relatively high cropping intensity. Then, the cropping intensity of the whole area may have dropped with tractor introduction.

There was a change in the cropping pattern of tractor farms in our sample. Most farms increased the proportion of their cultivated area sown to wheat in the winter season (4%), rice in the monsoon-summer season (1%), and to miscellaneous crops, such as vegetables, in both seasons (5%). At the same time, there were declines in the area sown to maize and cotton in summer (3%) and to fodder in both seasons (5%). Apart from the decline in fodder acreage, the other changes appear to be similar to those taking place generally in the district and cannot be attributed directly to tractorization.

Effects on tenants. Eighty-eight of the original 105 tenants lost their land when the landowners bought the first tractors. The average tenant farm size declined from 4.4 to 3.4 ha (Table 9). In most cases, tenant ejection took place in the year the tractor was purchased.

Effect on livestock. Because the tractor replaced the bullock in some farm operations, we would expect a decline in draft animals on tractor farms. There were

Table 8. Cropping intensity by farm size before and after tractor purchase.

Farm category (ha)	Cropping intensity		
	Before tractor	After tractor (1977/78)	Proportional change
Less than 10	104	141	1.36
10-19.5	135	138	1.02
20-39.5	138	146	1.06
40 and above	176	155	0.88
All farms	141	146	1.04

Table 9. Tenancy before tractor purchase and in 1978.

Kind of change in farm size	Farmers (no.)	Area leased out (ha)				Tenants (no.)		Av tenancy (ha)	
		Before tractor	1978	Difference	Percentage change	Before tractor	1978	Before tractor	1978
Increased	34	278	23	255	91	59	8	4.7	2.9
"New" farmers[a]	17	161	16	145	89	38	5	4.2	3.2
Total	51	439	39	400	91	97	13	4.5	3.0
No change	33	16	5	11	69	5	2	3.2	2.4
Decreased	4	7	13	6	72	3	2	2.4	6.3
Total	88	462	57	405	88	105	17	4.4	3.4

[a]Had not farmed before owning a tractor.

about 333 bullocks on the sample farms before tractor purchase (3.8/farm); in 1979 there remained 159 (1.8/farm). On the average, each tractor had replaced 2.0 bullocks. In the McInerney and Donaldson survey, the average number of bullocks per farm declined from 5.4 to 2.9 (2.5/tractor). However, farmers did not act uniformly: 12 sold all of their bullocks (54) after buying a tractor, 44 sold some bullocks and kept some (245 to 107), 10 kept their bullocks (30), 12 farmers had none before or after the tractor, and 10 actually increased their bullocks (4 to 22). Most farmers did not regard the tractor as a perfect substitute for bullocks in all farm operations. In particular, they preferred bullocks for chopping and carting fodder, planking, intercultural operations, cane-crushing, and line sowing. Only two farmers said that they kept bullocks as a standby when their tractors were being repaired.

There was little change in milk animal numbers. Apparently, farmers regarded draft and milk animals as distinct and a reduction in the number of draft animals did not lead to a corresponding increase in the milk herd.

Effect on labor. The tractor-farm survey in Faisalabad District did not obtain data on hired or family labor except to ask how many workers were employed on a full-time or permanent basis. Although the number for 1978 (184) was probably accurate, the pretractor number (164) spread over many years should be treated with caution. Using these numbers, there was an increase of around 12% in the number of permanently employed. Two factors complicate this simple arithmetic. First, only 71 of the 88 farmers were operating farms before buying their tractors and, therefore, the number of permanently hired laborers per farm fell by 8%. Second, because there was a 53% increase in the operated farm area, the number employed per cultivated hectare declined by 17%. Another complication was that 86 tenant families were expelled, substantially reducing the on-farm labor pool.

The 1979 survey of wheat threshing operations of traditional and mechanized farms near Multan obtained details of labor use during the harvesting-threshing season. Mechanization caused no change in the labor used for harvesting which was mainly contracted out and, except for carting the cut wheat to the threshing area, was not mechanized. Mechanization substantially reduced the use of labor for threshing. The differences between the traditional and mechanized sample farms — farm size, average area of wheat harvested (2.87 and 19.43 ha), and average yields (1.47 and 2.29 t/ha) — made direct comparisons tricky. Nonetheless, the orders of magnitude were clear. The traditional threshing method required an average of 3.26 days/ha for wheat and used 101 hours/ha of labor. The mechanical method required 0.74 day/ha and used 67 hours/ha. For traditional threshing, bullocks worked an average of 37.7 hours/ha of wheat threshed; on farms using mechanical threshing, the tractor and thresher were used 9.3 hours/ha.

Surprisingly, the operational costs for both methods were similar: $15.04/ha for traditional methods and $14.20/ha for thresher and tractor. However, the mechanical method doubled the cost of power and equipment and halved the labor cost. Therefore, mechanical wheat threshing reduced the amount of labor needed by about 36%, and reduced labor earnings by about 55%. From the farmer's point of view, the savings in labor cost were transferred mainly to fuel and machinery maintenance expenses.

Tractor use and development of a custom service market

The sample tractors were operated an average of 1,120 hours during the 12-month period: 58% on land preparation and cultivation, 20% on wheat threshing, 18% on carting and hauling work, and 4% on other jobs.

The considerable variation in tractor use was due to variation in the operated farm area (Table 10), the tractor attachments owned, and the extent to which the owner engaged in custom services. Clearly tractor use on the owners' farm was positively correlated with farm size, whereas providing custom services was negatively correlated with farm size. The type of custom service and the amount of time given to this enterprise depended on the equipment and attachments owned. Only 18 of the tractors in the survey were not used for custom jobs.

The development of the custom market in recent years is the most important change in farm mechanization. We have seen the development of a new class of entrepreneur who has invested heavily in farm machinery and has actively sought business. We were unable to measure the extent of this business or how profitable it was, but it is quite extensive and growing very rapidly.

Tractor repair and maintenance

Eighty-eight tractor-owning farmers, 47 private workshops, 11 manufacturers of farm machinery, 2 tractor dealers, 3 cooperative farm service centers, 2 general automobile workshops, and 16 spare parts dealers were interviewed in an attempt to evaluate the tractor repair and maintenance facilities in Faisalabad District. The ability of tractor-owning farmers to properly operate and maintain farm machines was very poor. The many private workshops scattered throughout the district offered a wide range of services, but most lacked appropriate tools and equipment. Skilled manpower was scarce both on and off the farm and the supply of spare parts was inadequate and costly.

Breakdowns. Fifty-nine percent of the tractors owned by the sample farmers had major breakdowns and repairs during 1978 — 25% of these occurred during the wheat threshing season. The average downtime was 14 days (range of 5-30 days). The frequency of breakdowns was greatest for tractors between 2 and 5 years old. Breakdowns of the hydraulic system, fuel pump, dynamo, clutch, steering mechanism, and water body were most common and often caused by misuse or poor maintenance. The average repair cost was $257 (ranging from $129 to $766), of which spare parts were the largest component.

Table 10. Tractor use by farm size.

Operated farm area[a] (ha)	Av hours of tractor operation/year	Tractor hours (%)	
		Owner's farm	Hire services
More than 40	1431	83	17
20-39.5	1126	80	20
10-19.5	1019	48	52
Less than 10	1059	27	73

[a]In 1978.

Farmers recognized that unskilled operators, often themselves, were the main cause of breakdowns. However, they also placed some blame on manufacturing defects, substandard parts, and adulterated or wrong lubricants. Farmers had poor technical knowledge about tractors. Few understood or followed manufacturers' instructions on periodic replacement of oil and filters, few owned even simple tool kits or could carry out minor repairs, and few had formal training in tractor driving and operation.

Repair facilities. In 1978, there were 146 private workshops, 3 dealers' workshops, 3 cooperative service centers, 1 government workshop, and a number of farm machinery manufacturers and general automobile workshops in Faisalabad District. Spare parts were available from 76 shops. Special service technicians — tire vulcanizers, radiator mechanics, battery specialists, dynamo and autoelectricians — and diesel-testing facilities were generally clustered with tractor workshops on the outskirt at most rural towns and Faisalabad City. Half of the workshops and spare parts shops had opened since 1975.

Ninety percent of repairs were carried out at private workshops, 5% at tractor dealers' workshops, 4% by the farmers themselves, and 1% at the government workshop in Faisalabad. None of the sample farmers patronized the cooperative service workshops. Private workshop mechanics had varied skills and experience as well as facilities to work in. Workshops were visited early in the study, assessed, and divided into four categories on the basis of the tools and equipment (Table 11). Forty-seven having 52 owner-mechanics were studied in detail.

The level of formal education of owner-mechanics was low, but most had attended short mechanics training courses such as those run by Millat Tractors. Seventy-three percent of the workshop owners had less than 2 years experience as mechanics. In the typical workshop, the owner was the only trained mechanic, although eight also employed mechanics. All workshops employed or attached "trainees," boys between the ages of 8 and 16. Of the 140 trainees attached to the sample workshops, 36% received no payment and the rest received $2-$15/month, depending on age and experience. Trainees constituted a cheap, but largely unskilled, work force while they obtained informal training and experience in tractor and other machinery repair. Employed mechanics earned $10-$40/month depending on experience. There was a fairly rapid turnover with employees predominantly moving to other workshops or opening their own. The sample workshops employed

Table 11. Type of workshop, investment in tools, and equipment, and number in category, Faisalabad, Pakistan, 1978.

| Workshop category | Tools, equipment[a] | Value ($) | | Workshop (no.) in | |
		Tools	Equipment	District	Sample
A	CT + SE	560	1600	25	8
B	IT + SE	300	1600	25	8
C	CT	370	–	31	10
D	IT	180	–	65	21
Total				146	47

[a]CT = Complete tool kit, SE = special equipment (e.g. lathe), IT = incomplete tool kit.

211 persons, comprising 52 owner mechanics, 11 family mechanics, 8 paid mechanics, and 140 trainees.

Of an estimated 2,000 repair and maintenance jobs completed in 1978, 525 were by type A workshops, 367 by type B, 778 by type C, and 330 by type D. The more complicated jobs, such as engine overhauling, went mainly to type A and B workshops. The higher job rate of type C workshops was due to their more frequent location in rural areas and willingness to provide on-farm services. Few workshops specialized in particular tractor makes or types of repairs. Seasonal peaks for tractor repair were in March-June and October-December when tractors were heavily engaged in plowing, threshing and carting. Forty percent of the workshops reported that they received as much work as they could handle. Most that could have taken more work were located in urban and rural town areas. Half of the workshops reported their ability to do many repair jobs was constrained by lack of appropriate tools and equipment. Many claimed to be willing to invest more if they could obtain credit on reasonable terms.

The three cooperative farm service centers in the district were very well equipped with tools, machine, workshop areas, and other facilities. These represented a total fixed investment of about $45,000. Charges were generally lower than at private workshops and some spare parts were stocked and sold at lower prices than at private shops. However, they had very little work. One center was not covering variable costs, the second turned in a small profit, and the third had been waiting about 4 years for electricity so work could start.

Spare parts supply. The widest range of tractor spare parts, particularly imported parts, was available from tractor and parts importers and assemblers in Lahore and tractor dealers. Faisalabad City tractor dealers and subdealers also maintained reasonable stocks, although they reported delays while parts were brought from Lahore. Most rural towns had spare parts shops, but these generally maintained very limited stocks of a narrow range of fast-moving parts. The three cooperative farm service centers maintained stocks of spares, but very few of the private workshops did.

Farmers and mechanics reported that parts were not always available even in Lahore and that they were often forced to substitute "inferior" locally made parts, and to adapt parts from other makes. Most farmers were willing to pay the higher costs for "genuine" parts. Prices for all parts were considerably higher in the rural town shops than in Faisalabad and Lahore.

CONCLUSION

Since 1970, the Pakistani Government has implemented a straightforward farm mechanization policy — to increase the availability of farm power through the importation and manufacture of four-wheel tractors, and the subsidization of credit for tractor purchases.

In practice, the number, makes, and models of imported tractors have been controlled and have varied from year to year according to foreign exchange allocations and special credit or trade arrangements with suppliers and supplying countries. It appears that the demand for tractors, although partly conditioned by government allocations of credit through the Agricultural Development Bank of Pakistan, exceeds supply and that the distribution process greatly favors farmers at the top end of the traditional power structure. The recent provision of a limited amount of subsidized credit to small farmers is too small and too late to alter the overall balance. However small farmers appear to provide an expanding market for used tractors, using funds obtained through foreign remittances and sellers' credit.

Although it is government policy to increase the efficiency of tractor use and the level of farm productivity by encouraging the adoption of cultivation attachments, that policy has not been implemented as vigorously as the simpler activity of importing tractors. The recent, rapidly increasing demand for and local fabrication of tractor-driven wheat threshers is the only significant change of interest in attachments since 1970. While subsidized credit has always been provided for tractor purchases, the ADBP only began making loans for thresher purchases in 1979.

By controlling imports, the government has effectively removed competition among tractor sellers, resulting in poor service, inadequate supplies of spare parts, and a lack of interest in training in tractor use and machinery maintenance facilities. Repair and maintenance services have developed rapidly in the private sector, but facilities generally are poorly equipped with tools and technical expertise. Likewise, most tractor owners have little technical knowledge of tractor use and maintenance. However, in the present situation of relatively small tractor numbers and limited annual imports, private gains from tractor ownership are high enough to more than compensate for high maintenance costs and inefficient tractor use.

Although there is evidence of high returns to farmers on investments in tractors and attachments, there is little evidence of appreciable social benefits. Tractors do not appear to have contributed to significant increases in farm productivity, either by bringing uncultivated land into production or by increasing the intensity of cultivation and crop yields. On the other hand, the opportunity costs of foreign exchange allocated for tractor imports and fuel, social hardship and reduced earnings of the rural landless, and the reinforcement of an inequitable traditional rural power structure indicate the very high cost of the present program.

REFERENCES CITED

Farm Mechanization Committee. 1969. Report on the farm mechanization survey, 1968. Government of Pakistan, Planning and Development Department, Lahore.

Farm Mechanization Committee. 1970. Farm mechanization in West Pakistan. Government of Pakistan, Ministry of Agriculture and Works, Islamabad.

McInerney, J. P., and G. F. Donaldson. 1975. The consequences of farm tractors in Pakistan. World Bank Staff Working Paper 210.

Pakistan Government Planning Commission. 1978. The fifth five year plan (1978-83). Islamabad.

INNOVATION IN THE PHILIPPINE AGRICULTURAL MACHINERY INDUSTRY

K. W. Mikkelsen and N. N. Langam

Data from a partially completed survey were used to investigate innovative activity and product-improving technological change in the Philippine agricultural machinery industry. Most firms had one or more persons engaged in inventing new products, improving products, and improving production methods, usually on an informal basis. Nearly all firms had made significant improvements.

In most discussions of the consequences of agricultural technology, private agents in agriculture and related industries are considered to have a very minor role in generating new technology. New technology is developed outside the agricultural sector and can either be accepted at some rate and to some degree, or rejected. This view may be appropriate for basic agricultural research which, because private agents lack either the incentive or capacity, must be undertaken by public and quasi-public institutions. In contrast, a new machine, in addition to being accepted or rejected, may be modified and adapted to local conditions. This paper explores innovative activity and product-improving technological changes among agricultural machinery manufacturers in the Philippines.

DESCRIPTION OF SAMPLE FIRMS

The data used for this preliminary report were obtained from interviews with 47 agricultural machinery manufacturing firms. The sample was drawn from two sources. First, the survey was to cover all firms which have actively participated in

Yale University and The International Rice Research Institute.

the Industrial Extension Program developed by the Agricultural Engineering Department of the International Rice Research Institute (IRRI). Actively participating firms were defined as those having received designs of one or more machines developed at IRRI and having produced at least one commercially. Of the 37 firms initially identified, the interviews revealed only 27 were active participants. Data from the 10 other firms were retained for added information. The second source of sample firms was a list of about 75 non-IRRI agricultural machinery manufacturers compiled from several directories. After stratifying by region, a systematic sample of 25 firms was drawn. Ten of these firms have been interviewed to date. Figure 1 shows the geographic dispersion of the sample.

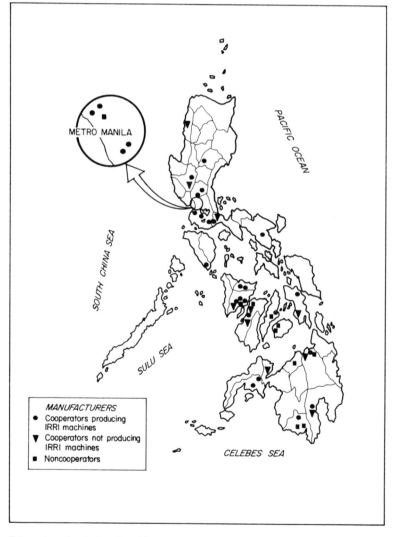

1. Location of agricultural machinery manufacturers in the Philippines.

Ninety-one percent of the sample firms manufactured more than one product. The most common agricultural machines were rice threshers and two-wheel tractors (Table 1); others were rice dryers, rice and maize mills, and maize shellers. Many firms also produced furniture and jeep bodies, or performed metalworking services. Some firms retailed machinery usually made by foreign manufacturers. Firm size showed considerable diversity (Tables 2, 3). Employment ranged from several one-man shops to three firms each employing more than 100 workers. Despite their numerical dominance, small firms accounted for only 16.3% of total employment, whereas the 8 firms employing 50 or more provided 52.3%. More than half of the firms employed fewer than 20 workers. A similar picture emerged in sales. Twelve of the 40 firms reported sales of $20,000 or less in 1980; the median value was $37,467. Ten large firms, four of which were also in the largest employment group, reported sales of more than $500,000, and together they captured 87% of 1980 sales.

Table 1. Common agricultural machinery products.

Product	Firms producing (no.)	Av no. of units produced	Av price ($)
IRRI portable thresher	18	71	696
IRRI axial-flow thresher	15	58	2,548
IRRI two-wheel tractor	15	102	754
Non-IRRI two-wheel tractor	7	167	1,247
Blower	6	50	67
Non-IRRI thresher	5	47	1,002

Table 2. Distribution of firms by level of employment.

Range	Firms (no.)	Employees (no.)	Employees/firm
1-9 employees	16	87	5.4
10-19 employees	10	126	10.6
20-49 employees	13	411	31.6
50 and above	8	685	85.6
Total	47	1,309	27.9

Table 3. Distribution of firms by sales.

Range (thousand $)	Firms (no.)	Sales (thousand $)	
		Total	Average
Up to 20	12	76	6.4
21-40	12	380	31.6
41-100	6	396	65.9
101-500	6	1,936	322.6
501 and above	4	3,658	914.5
Total	40	6,446	(av) 161.1

INNOVATIVE ACTIVITY

The most common measure of innovative activity is expenditure on research and development (R&D). Seventeen of the sample firms reported some R&D expenditure in 1980 (Table 4). R&D activities and firm size appeared to be positively correlated and no firms with annual sales of $20,000 or less reported R&D. However, these figures probably understate the amount of innovative activity, particularly among smaller firms where R&D is frequently not explicitly organized as a separate activity within the firm and may not be identified or reported. Measure of innovative activity which includes informal innovative effort, sometimes callled "blue-collar R&D," was obtained by asking each firm how many persons performed various technical functions within the firm, and what percentage of their time was spent on each function in 1980. Three of these functions, corresponding to the central purposes of formal R&D, were inventing new products, improving products, and improving production methods (Table 5). Almost 25% of the firms made no effort to invent new products, nearly all attempted to improve existing products or processes. Only 2 of the 45 responding firms reported no innovative activity. Summing the three activities, an average of about one man-year/firm was devoted to technology improvement. Unlike the R&D measure, which indicated that less than half of the firms participated in innovative activity, the function-oriented measure showed that even the smallest firms participated. This appears consistent with the evidence on product improvement.

Table 4. Distribution of firms performing R&D, by firm sales.

Range (thousand $)	Firms (no.)	Firms (no.) reporting R&D
Up to 20	11	0
21-40	12	5
41-100	6	3
101-500	6	5
501 and above	4	3
Total	39	16

Table 5. Allocation of resources to various forms of innovative activity.

Allocation (man-yr)	Firms (no.) engaged in given innovative activity		
	Inventing new products	Improving products	Improving production methods
0	10	4	3
0.0-0.25	19	28	25
0.26-0.5	7	6	9
0.51-1.0	6	4	5
1.01-2.0	0	1	0
2.01 and more	2	2	2
Total	44	45	44
Average level (man-yr)	.33	.35	.34

To identify the important resources used in innovation, firms were asked to rate sources of technology and new ideas on a scale from 1 (not important at all) to 4 (extremely important). The average rating for customers (3.5) was the highest. Customers frequently identified problems in machine performance and offered suggestions for improvements based on personal experience with the products. In some cases, features requested by the buyer of a custom-built machine proved so successful that they were incorporated into the standard design. The second ranking source was technical personnel with the firm (3.3). In most cases, innovative activity was not carried out by specialized personnel. The owner or manager of the firm was frequently involved, as were production supervisors and foremen. Formal technical training among the 208 persons reportedly performing any of the innovative functions included 4 MS degrees, 47 BS degrees, and some training past high school for an additional 48 persons. IRRI was ranked third as a source of new technology (3.0). In addition to supplying machine designs, IRRI responds to requests from cooperating firms with advice on production management and assistance in product improvements initiated by the firm. Less important sources of technology were suppliers, subcontractors, non-IRRI consultants, workers, trade journals, and patent documents.

PRODUCT IMPROVEMENT

The success of innovative efforts in generating new technology was investigated through information collected about product improvements. Each firm was asked to list all changes made in its four main agricultural machinery products since the beginning of 1976. When possible, this list was supplemented by, and checked against, an actual examination of the current product. Forty-two of 46 firms made at least one change (Table 6).

Changes can be classified as minor or major. A typical minor change was alteration of material specifications. Other minor changes included modifying the shape of various parts or the configuration of parts on the machine, and adding parts or features to enhance the machine functions. Some major changes required considerable redesign. One indication that a firm's product changes were not trivial was the number of patents held. Patents are only granted for changes meeting certain standards of novelty, usefulness, and significance. Sixty patents had been issued to 18 firms, and applications were pending for another eight. An additional 27 changes

Table 6. Distribution of firms by number of product changes.

Number of changes	Firms (no.)	Av no. of changes/firm
0	4	0.0
1-5	22	3.0
6-10	11	7.3
11-15	7	11.7
16-20	1	17.0
21 or more	1	23.0
Total	46	5.8

were judged by both the authors and the innovating firms to be patentable, although no application had been made. These patented and patentable changes accounted for 35% of the listed changes.

The extent to which these changes indicate activity among agricultural machinery firms is also influenced by the degree of overlap or duplication of changes between firms. Several features of the industry suggested that the changes made by one firm may not be very different from those made by others. First, it was apparent from the survey that most firm managers were quite familiar with the competing designs sold in their region. Second, firms had little reservation about copying designs. Even though many firms held patents, few considered it worthwhile to prosecute for patent infringement. Third, firms felt a great deal of competitive pressure. Seventy percent indicated that their customers as well as potential customers would have little or no difficulty finding an alternative supply source if they stopped production. Under such conditions, rapid dissemination of profitable innovations would be anticipated.

To investigate their individuality, a list was compiled of the changes made in the most common products — the IRRI-designed two-wheel tractor, portable thresher, and axial-flow thresher. Individual changes were grouped by feature, or component. For example, all changes on the threshing drum were grouped together, all changes on the blower formed a separate group. The results (Table 7) showed that, for each of the three products, most changes were made by a very few firms. This high degree of individuality actually understated the situation since firms changing the same component often made very different improvements. This individuality can probably be attributed to the segmented nature of the agricultural machinery market. Most firms sell to a local, not national or international, market. Localities differ in agricultural conditions such as soil type, water patterns, and in customer preferences. Consequently, a change that enhances product performance or desirability in one area would not necessarily be effective elsewhere.

As noted earlier, firms rely heavily on their customers as a source of new ideas. One point of interaction between manufacturers and users is direct sales. All but six of the sample firms made at least some sales directly to end users, and 68% sold 50% or more of their output by this method. The industry has responded to contacts with the local market by developing a variety of differentiated products appealing to

Table 7. Distribution of component changes by firms.[a]

	Component changes (no.)		
	Two-wheel tractor	Portable thresher	Axial-flow thresher
Firms (no.)	11	14	13
By 1 firm	11	5	11
By 2 firms	3	5	2
By 3 firms	3	4	3
By 4 or more firms	2	4	3
Total	19	18	19

[a]Numbers in parentheses indicate the number of firms that made changes in the given unit.

different needs and tastes, instead of highly homogeneous products. This allows farmers and other users to choose the machine with features most suited to their conditions.

CONCLUSION

Any mechanical technology introduced to the agricultural sector is likely to be altered. In a sample of Philippine agricultural machinery manufacturers, almost all firms engaged in some technology-improving activities. Most firms made improvements in existing machine designs, and different firms tended to make different improvements. Over time, such private efforts can help to increase the level of technology and to adapt it to diverse agricultural conditions.

ECONOMIC ANALYSIS OF THE FARM MACHINERY INDUSTRY AND TRACTOR CONTRACTOR BUSINESS IN THAILAND

S. Wattanutchariya

This paper provides information on the local farm machinery industry in Thailand and looks at the economics of farm machinery hire services. The local industry, developed during the past 2 decades, is now facing strong competition within the country and from abroad. The tractor contractor has provided access to farm machinery throughout the country. Custom services are profitable but because of increases in operating costs and competition, contractors' profits are declining and farmers are paying higher custom rates.

In most developing countries, food policy has aimed at increasing production through introduction of modern technologies. These include the development of new crop varieties, improved cultural practices, irrigation systems, and farm mechanization. Although mechanization may be blamed for increasing unemployment, it is frequently justified because it permits faster and more efficient cultivation, particularly of heavier and more difficult soils. This may lead to increases in cropping intensity and employment.

In developing countries where labor is abundant, attempts to introduce higher levels of mechanization should be preceded by investigation of both social and economic repercussions. Many studies on these questions have been conducted in Thailand. Two specific aspects, the development of the local farm machinery industry and the economics of providing farm machinery custom services, are investigated in this paper.

USE OF FARM MACHINERY

According to Kitdhakorn (1971), one of the pioneers of modern farming in Thailand, the first tractor was imported during World War I for experimental use in the

Kasetsart University.

rice fields near Bangkok, but was too heavy for the soil conditions. In 1920, Kitdhakorn used a tractor for cultivating upland crops in Pracheub Kirikhan, about 200 km south of Bangkok.

After World War II, heavy mechanical equipment was needed to open up new land for cultivation of upland crops. This led to the importation of farm tractors. In 1957, the Department of Customs recorded the import of 267 tractors, mostly from England. It was not until 1970 that imported farm tractors were recorded separately from other tractors. Imports peaked at 6,161 in 1977 (Table 1). The decline thereafter was mainly due to an increase in the number of locally produced or assembled tractors. The Thailand Office of Agricultural Economics (1980) reported that there were 230,591 two-wheel tractors, 31,158 small four-wheel tractor, 33,285 full-size tractors, and 8,000 motor rollers during the 1979-80 crop year, an average of 1 tractor/51.4 ha.

DEVELOPMENT OF THE FARM MACHINERY INDUSTRY

The Engineering Division, Department of Agriculture, Ministry of Agriculture and Cooperatives, has long been involved in developing and testing farm machinery adapted to the Thai environment. Examples of machinery developed are the well-known Tebariddhi pump in 1955 and the "Iron Buffalo" in 1958. Several models of the "Iron Buffalo" were developed during the early 1960's and sold by a private company (Taenkam 1980). Due to the small scale of operation, relatively high costs, and competition from other local and imported machines, the company ceased operation in 1967.

In addition to government agencies, various private firms have undertaken research and development of farm machinery, in particular power tiller or two-wheel tractor. The design was originally simplified from a Japanese power tiller. In the 1980 survey, several firms accredited Singkru Utsahagam at Prapradaeng as their source of design. That firm's first two-wheel tractor was a modification, to suit local conditions, of a Mitsubishi tiller imported in 1963. These tractors were first marketed in the area in 1965 and gained popularity due to the low price compared to imported machines, and their ability to perform well under local conditions. Because this tractor design is simple and requires no special manufacturing technology, many firms have started manufacture in Prapradaeng and other provinces.

Table 1. Farm tractors imported or locally produced during 1975-79.[a]

Item	Number				
	1975	1976	1977	1978	1979
Imported farm tractors	4,231	5,257	6,161	4,298	3,559
Small four-wheel tractors (locally produced)	2,582	2,914	4,568	5,631	4,920
Two-wheel tractors (locally produced)	27,860	31,766	49,722	52,281	54,124

[a] Sources: Department of Customs; estimates by Thailand Office of Agricultural Economics, Ministry of Agriculture and Cooperatives.

Even though the demand for small, locally produced tractors is increasing, there is considerable competition among producers. Many large producers, who have access to credit and modern equipment, are more capable than smaller firms of producing at low cost. In addition, the marketing and managerial abilities of the owner are important for success. The survey, found that many firms, especially in the Prapradaeng area, have ceased doing business because of competition.

The development of an alternative to the "Iron Buffalo" started a few years after the local two-wheel tractor was widely accepted. A simple four-wheel tractor was developed by a group of firms in Ayutthaya by adding two more wheels so that the driver could operate from a seat instead of walking. The design was modified later to include gear and hydraulic systems similar to those of imported tractors. Development of small four-wheel tractors is still in progress, but the two-wheel tractor design remains unchanged.

In general, a firm will produce more than one type of farm machine so as to fully utilize its resouces and to meet seasonal market demands. For example, a firm may produce small tractors between January and June, before the planting season, and rice threshing machines and water pumps during the rest of the year. According to the survey, which covered most major firms in Bangkok metropolis and the nearby provinces, more than 33% of the firms produce only two-wheel tractors, 20% produce two-wheel and four-wheel tractors, 20% produce two-wheel tractors and rice threshers, and 9% produce all three machines (Table 2). For subsequent analysis, firms were divided into three types based on their main product as defined by value:

- *Type 1 firms* (23 of 35) produced mainly two-wheel tractors.
- *Type 2 firms* (7) produced mainly four-wheel tractors.
- *Type 3 firms* (5) produced mainly threshing machines.

The former activity of the manufacturer is in Table 3. Firm size in each type ranged from a few to more than 100 workers. Table 4 shows the number of firms classified by the number of workers and the operating period during the year. The survey showed that more than half of the firms produced throughout the year, but some reduced the number of workers in the off-season, maintaining sufficient skilled labor to produce tractors essential for stock.

Table 2. Surveyed firms classified by type of machinery.

Type of machinery	Firms	
	No.	%
Two-wheel tractor	12	34
Four-wheel tractor	1	3
Maize thresher	5	14
Both two-wheel and four-wheel tractors	7	20
Both two-wheel tractor and rice thresher	7	20
Two-wheel, four-wheel tractors and rice thresher	3	9
Total	35	100

Table 3. Frequency of former activities by manufacturers.

Occupation	Manufacturers[a] (no.)			
	Type 1 firm	Type 2 firm	Type 3 firm	Total
Metal worker	6	4	3	13
Machinery repairman	2	2	3	7
Farm machinery dealer	3	1	–	4
Metal dealer	2	1	–	3
Dealer in other products	6	–	–	6
Farmer	2	–	–	2
Others[b]	9	2	3	14
Total	30	10	9	49

[a]Type 1 firm produced mainly two-wheel tractors; type 2 firm, four-wheel tractors; and type 3 firm, threshing machines, [b]Rice miller, automotive repairman, bicycle repairman, water pump manufacturer, etc.

Table 4. Firms classified by number of workers and operating periods.

Item	Firms[a] (no.)			
	Type 1	Type 2	Type 3	Total
Number of workers				
Less than 20	11	2	1	14
20-39	5	1	3	9
40-100	6	1	1	8
More than 100	1	3	--	4
Total	23	7	5	35
Operating period				
Throughout the year	13	6	–	19
By order	6	1	1	8
Seasonal	4	–	4	8
Total	23	7	5	35

[a]Type 1 firm produced mainly two-wheel tractors; type 2 firm, four-wheel tractors; and type 3 firm, threshing machines.

SOURCES OF DESIGN CHANGES

There has never been any patent law covering farm machinery in Thailand so firms are free to copy from abroad or from each other. Table 5 shows design sources reported by the sample firms. Although several firms reported designing their own machines many admitted copying from other sources, especially from Singkru Utsahagam. In fact, many of those who claimed to be designers probably copied a machine and made some minor changes. It was also found that many firms introduced changes based on customers' recommendations (Table 6). Design changes were most frequently made to improve performance and suit a customer's needs. Some firms reported changes in design to eliminate unnecessary costs.

PRODUCTION PROCESS AND COST OF PRODUCTION OF FARM MACHINERY

The main tractor components produced by the firms are body parts such as wheels, engine housing, chassis, and handle. Other parts, such as engine, chain, and bearing,

Table 5. Frequency of sources of design for machines.

Sources of design	Frequency (no.)				
	Two-wheel tractor	Two-wheel tractor with clutch	Four-wheel tractor	Rice thresher	Maize thresher
Any brand in the market	7	1	1	—	1
Another brand in the same location	2	—	—	2	2
Another brand in different location	15	2	3	2	—
Foreign design	1	2	3	—	2
Own design	1	3	6	5	—
IRRI design	1	—	—	4	—
Others[a]	3	—	2	—	1
Total	30	8	15	13	6

[a]Division of Agricultural Engineering, mechanic previously employed by another firm, etc.

Table 6. Source of changes in design and reason for changing.

Item	Firms[a] (no.)			
	Type 1	Type 2	Type 3	Total
Sources of changes				
Recommended by customer	19	3	5	27
Owner	6	1	1	8
Followed other firms	6	–	–	6
Copied from imported machine	1	–	1	2
Own mechanic	–	1	2	3
Others	2	1	–	3
Total	34	6	9	49
Reasons for changing				
Reduced cost	5	2	–	7
Improved performance	20	2	5	27
Suited customer's need	8	2	3	13
Better looks	4	4	–	8
Others	2	1	–	3
Total	39	11	8	58

[a]Type 1 firm produced mainly two-wheel tractors; type 2 firm, four-wheel tractors; and type 3 firm, threshing machines.

are purchased. Machines used can be very simple. A small firm may have a welder, lathe, sprayer, and acetylene cutter, while a large firm may employ more labor-saving machines such as hydraulic press, shapers, steel roller, honing machine, electric power drive, and sprocket wheel cutter (Pinthong 1974).

Estimated costs of production of two-wheel and four-wheel tractors are shown in Table 7. Excluding the diesel engine, steel, which is the main input for two-wheel tractors, accounts for 50% of the cost. The cost of an 8-hp diesel engine is around $650. Total cost of two-wheel tractor with engine is $849 compared to $1,500 for an imported two-wheel tractor. However, imported tractors are better built, lighter, and perform more functions. A small four-wheel tractor, including the 15-hp diesel engine, costs around $2,150. The sale price of the imported small four-wheel tractor is around $3,650. In general, there is more variation in the cost and design of four-wheel tractors than of two-wheel tractors.

MARKETING OF FARM MACHINERY

Marketing of local farm machinery is very important. Because product differentiation among two-wheel tractors is low, firms have to use special techniques to gain popularity. Machines manufactured outside the Bangkok Metropolitan Area were produced predominantly for the local market and sold directly rather than through dealers. The large firms in Bangkok and one firm in Prathum Thani sold for cash or on credit through dealers throughout the country. Dealers were crucial to the firms because they also provided useful customer feedback on potential design changes. Products from large firms were usually cheaper because of economies of scale in mass production. Smaller firms maintained their market share by having close contact with the customers.

Table 7. Estimated cost of production of two-wheel and four-wheel tractors.[a]

Item	Two-wheel tractor Cost ($)	%	Four-wheel tractor Cost ($)	%
Steel plate	66	34	167	15
Steel rod	29	15	47	4
Cast iron	–	–	24	2
Cast aluminum	–	–	123	11
Lubricated oil	15	7	10	1
Bearing	16	8	61	5
Chains	17	9	37	3
Hydraulic pump	–	–	126	11
Other parts	24	12	233	21
Wage	11	6	87	8
Electricity and fuel	2	1	52	5
Depreciation	1	1	52	5
Other expenses	7	3	70	6
Production tax	7	3	39	3
Tax on machinery	–	–	24	0
Subtotal (without engine)	195	100	1132	100
Diesel engine	654	–	1037	–
(8 hp and 15 hp)				
Total cost	849	–	2169	–

[a]Source: estimates by Industrial Service Institute 1981.

At the time of the study, there was no serious competition among four-wheel tractor manufacturers because there was excess demand and each firm was producing close to its full capacity. Most four-wheel tractors were sold direct to farmers growing broadcast rice in the Central Plains because such tractors were too heavy to perform well in wet paddy fields. Farmers who transplant paddy prefer two-wheel tractors.

The foreign market is the next logical step for large manufacturers. Some have sent trial shipments to Indonesia, but improvements are necessary before they are accepted.

ROLE OF GOVERNMENT IN THE FARM MACHINERY INDUSTRY

Two government agencies are involved in the extension of farm machinery (Mongkoltanatas 1981). The Industrial Service Institute (ISI), Ministry of Industry, assists manufacturers by providing technical training and advisory services to owners, managers, and workers. ISI also organized the Forum of Tractor Manufacturers of Thailand in 1977. The objectives of the forum are to support local farm machinery manufacturers and to improve production techniques. At present the 40 members are mostly in the central region. The second agency — the Agricultural Engineering Division (AED) of the Ministry of Agriculture and Cooperatives — assists manufacturing firms in testing and modifying new products. The survey showed 40% of the firms received government assistance in the form of investment credit, machine design, tax exemption for equipment and management, and technical training.

MAJOR PROBLEMS AND SUGGESTED SOLUTIONS

Major problems facing the local farm machinery industry and solutions suggested by producers were as follows:

1. *Financial.* Forty percent of the respondents, especially smaller firms, reported financial problems, in particular, the difficulty of obtaining low interest loans from the government. It was suggested that the government should encourage small firms by providing sufficient funds to help reduce production costs and lower the price of machinery to farmers.

2. *Technological difficulties.* Although there are no patent laws and firms could copy designs, the unavailability of suitable technology was considered an important problem.

3. *Lack of skilled labor.* Most workers gained experience through on-the-job training. Many skilled workers had been attracted to the Middle East and training was needed for young unskilled workers.

4. *Marketing.* The demand for machinery depends on crop yield and price. Because these are variable, manufacturers must be ready to respond to changes.

There were also minor problems, such as lack of proper equipment and unfair taxation (Industrial Service Institute 1981). For example, imported materials are taxed higher than imported farm machinery (13.55% and 11.27% tax for local two-wheel and four-wheel tractors, and 8.85% tax for imported machines).

In conclusion, the farm machinery industry in Thailand has been developed by private rather than government effort, but requires government assistance and protection for its continuation. If the goal of the government is to induce mechanization, it should support local farm machinery manufacture because these machines are inexpensive, simple, and designed to fit local conditions. Standardization of farm machinery for export markets, may be necessary but this will raise production cost to some extent. Taxation of imported machines and materials should also be revised if the government wants to generate employment and reduce the trade deficit.

ROLE OF THE TRACTOR CONTRACTOR IN FARM MECHANIZATION

Tractor contractors have played an important role in farm mechanization. Farms average 4 ha and most farmers cannot afford to own tractors. Contractor services, using full-size tractors, are mainly for cultivation of dryland for upland crops and broadcast rice. Contract services are also available for transporting and threshing, while farmers use their own bullocks for planting and weeding.

Contractor characteristics and services

Some tractor owners offering contract services travel more than 100 km for plowing during the off-season. A contractor survey was carried out during April and May 1980 in Phra Buddhabaht, Pak Chong, and Bang Pa In. The first two are major upland crop growing areas and the third is the broadcast rice area where most contractors are located. Thirty-four contractors, owning 48 tractors, were contacted. Of the 48 tractors, 22 were purchased new. Seventy-six percent of the contractors were rice or maize growers, 15% were upland crop middlemen, and the rest were general merchants. The average landholding was 14 ha. Two contractors operated only contract services.

Most contractors serviced neighboring areas after finishing their own work. Contracts were usually made directly with farmers and the custom rate was determined by soil conditions and the contract market situation. Some were made through commission agents, who looked for customers in nearby areas. The number of tractor owners is increasing and some contractors travel in groups to other provinces to find new customers.

Fuel is the most important factor in the contracting business. Because only a part of this increase can be passed on to the farmers, rising prices and shortages that increase operating cost discourage contractors from traveling long distances for customers.

Work and revenue from owning a tractor

Tractors plowed an average of 176 ha in 1979, 29 ha (17%) of which was owned land and 147 ha (83%) was contract (Table 8). The work averaged 432 hours. Contractors in Bang Pa In utilized their tractors more than those in the two other areas; however, the total revenue per tractor was less because of lower custom rates. The 1979 custom rate for plowing was $22/ha for upland and $11/ha for paddy land. That year, the contractors received an average total revenue of $3,077, 88% from plowing and the rest from activities such as threshing and transportation of farm produce. In Phra Buddhabaht, 96% of the revenue was from plowing.

Cost of operation and profitability

The cost of operation can be divided into cash and noncash costs. Cash costs, which refer to actual outlays such as fuel, oil, driver, maintenance, etc. accounted for 75% of total cost (Table 9). The cost of maintenance and repairs was the largest (41%)

Table 8. Average amount of work and revenue per tractor in 1979.

Item	Phra Buddhabaht	Pak Chong	Bang Pa In	Average
Area plowed (ha)				
Own land	25	25	40	29
Service	167	93	196	147
Total	192	117	237	176
Length of plowing (h)				
Own land	47	85	61	67
Service	352	319	446	365
Total	399	404	506	432
Revenue from plowing ($)				
Own land	347	575	466	465
Service	2672	1933	2059	2229
Total	3019	2508	2525	2694
Revenue from other activities ($)				
Own land	61	111	215	121
Service	45	627	40	262
Total	106	738	255	383
Total revenue ($)				
Own land	408	685	681	586
Service	2718	2560	2099	2491
Total	3126	3245	2780	3077

Table 9. Cost structure and profitability of tractors in 1979.

Item	Costs and returns ($)			
	Phra Buddhabaht	Pak Chong	Bang Pa In	Whole sample
Non-cash costs				
Depreciation	120	330	34	176
Opportunity cost of investment (8%)[a]	471	463	530	484
Opportunity cost of owner	29	50	53	43
Subtotal	620	843	617	703
Cash costs				
Repair and maintenance	1264	1242	673	1096
Fuel	988	692	593	782
Oil	62	143	81	94
Driver	109	139	168	136
Others	14	13	76	31
Subtotal	2437	2229	1591	2139
Total cost	3057	3072	2208	2842
Total revenue	3125	3245	2781	3077
Net return over cash cost	688	1016	1191	938
Net profit	68	173	573	236
Return from investment (%)	8.3	12.7	14.5	11.5

[a]Prevailing interest rate on bank savings accounts.

expense because most tractors had been operating for more than 5 years in poor soil conditions and required regular repairs. The cost of fuel accounted for nearly 28% of the total cost. As mentioned earlier, plowing land for broadcast rice is easier than for upland crops. So, tractor operation cost was much lower in Bang Pa In than in the two other areas, and therefore even though the revenue within the year was lower, the contractors made more profit.

Break-even point analysis
Annual tractor use required for economic viability can be evaluated by break-even point analysis (Fordson 1959). Because the tractors surveyed were used for a wide range of activities, each with varying contract rates, no common unit could be defined for measuring output. The analysis was therefore limited to use for plowing and fixed costs were determined in proportion to total use. Break-even points were estimated for each region and for the entire sample.

The results (Table 10) show the whole sample break-even point as 116 ha, while the actual average area plowed was 176 ha. For each region, the break-even area plowed was also less than the actual. It is reasonable to conclude that contractors are, on the average, making a profit from their operations.

Table 10. Break-even point of using tractor for land preparation in 1979.

Location	Total fixed cost ($)	Average variable cost ($/ha)	Average revenue ($/ha)	Break-even point (ha)	Actual (ha)
Phra Buddhabaht	509	12.20	15.74	146	192
Pak Chong	593	15.30	21.35	98	117
Bang Pa In	499	6.65	10.65	131	237
Whole sample	538	11.04	15.30	116	176

CONCLUSION

The tractor contractor has helped increase agricultural productivity by expanding new cultivated area and speeding up cultivation. This is beneficial to tractor owners and users because few owners can economically justify tractor ownership without contract operations. At present, tractor owners are making profits. However, with increasing competition and rising costs of operation, investment in tractors may not be worthwhile in the future unless sufficient demand for contractor services can be assured. Cost increases for fuel and spare parts have increased custom rates, and therefore costs of production. It is expected that there will be some substitution of buffalo for machines. Unless ways can be found to either increase yields or reduce other costs, there will be pressure on the government to increase crop prices.

REFERENCES CITED

Fordson, J. C. 1959. Break-even points for harvesting machines. University of Georgia, Georgia. 91 p.

Industrial Service Institute. 1981. Small tractor industry [in Thai]. Ministry of Industry, Bangkok, Thailand. 12 p.

Kitdhakorn, M. C. S. 1971. The use of farm machinery in Thailand [in Thai]. Pages 132-153 *in* Society of Social Science, ed. A report by and about M. C. Sithiporn Kitdhakorn. Sivaporn Press, Bangkok, Thailand.

Mongkoltanatas, J. 1981. Survey of agricultural machinery manufacturers. Agricultural Engineering Division, Ministry of Agriculture and Cooperative, Bangkok, Thailand. 9 p.

Pinthong, J. 1974. Economics of small tractor production in Thailand. MS, Faculty of Economics, Thammasat University, Bangkok, Thailand. 76 p.

Taenkam, P. 1980. The small tractor industry. MS, Faculty of Economics, Thammasat University, Bangkok, Thailand. 211 p.

Thailand Office of Agricultural Economics, Ministry of Agriculture. 1980. Small tractor industry in Thailand, Bangkok, Thailand. 25 p.

PRODUCTIVITY GROWTH OF THE AGRICULTURAL MACHINERY INDUSTRY IN THAILAND

Paitoon Wiboonchutikula

The rate of total factor productivity growth (TFPG) of the agricultural machinery industry in Thailand from the initial year of production to 1979 was estimated using data from two sources: 1) survey and interview of large and medium-sized firms, and 2) aggregate census data. Estimation from the first source showed the TFPG rates of all firms increased until 1976, then declined. Estimation from the second source showed the rate was small compared with that in developed countries and other manufacturing industries in Thailand.

One immediate impact of farm mechanization in Thailand has been the growth of the tractor manufacturing industry. The number of firms grew from a few in the mid-1960s to more than 100 in 1980, employing over 2,000 workers. Production grew about 16% annually. Growth came from two sources: the increase in resources used and an increase in the productivity of these resources which can be measured as total factor productivity growth (TFPG). This paper measures and analyzes TFPG of the agricultural machinery industry in Thailand. Basically, TFPG can be measured by subtracting the average of the rates of growth of real inputs, properly weighted, from the rate of growth of real output. For developed countries such as the USA (Solow 1957, Christensen and Jorgenson 1970, Kendrick 1973, and Denison 1974) and Japan (Jorgenson and Ezaki 1973, and Nishimizu and Hulton 1978), measured TFPG accounts for more than 50% of the rate of growth of real output of all manufacturing industries. Due to data limitations, there are few TFPG studies for developing countries.

DEVELOPMENT OF THE TRACTOR INDUSTRY

Small farm tractors were introduced from Japan in the mid-1950s. In the mid-1960s, local firms modified and started to manufacture the Japanese designs. They were

Department of Economics, University of Minnesota.

readily accepted because they were more suited to local soil conditions, easier to operate and repair, and less expensive than imported tractors. Since the late 1960s, with increases in farm incomes, higher food prices, and increases in agricultural wages, the industry has expanded rapidly. Nowadays many farmers own tractors and about 90% of total sales are produced domestically.

Tractor production in Thailand is labor-intensive and the market is free from government intervention. Other than the common business taxes, which are applied to all industries, subsidies and international trade protection are negligible. Local production is also competitive. Firms are numerous, products are similar, and entry is relatively easy. With some experience in machine shops and an initial investment of about $4,000 on machinery and equipment, production can start.

Both two-wheel power tillers and small four-wheel tractors are produced in Thailand. The two-wheel power tillers are equipped with 5- to 9-hp imported diesel engines and the four-wheel tractors with 10 hp and larger engines. About 85% of tractors used by Thai farmers are power tillers. In 1980, the survey year, there were about 99 tractor-producing firms, 79 producing two-wheel tractors only, 2 producing four-wheel tractors only, and 18 producing both. Eighty percent of the firms were located in the central region, and more than 70% of these were in the greater metropolitan areas, which provide both a better infrastructure and better access to raw materials.

The firms were placed into small, medium, and large categories. Most of the 62 small firms, producing less than 300 units/year and employing 2-10 workers, were located near farming areas. Their principal activity was assembling parts and components bought from others. Twenty-three medium firms produced 300-1,000 units annually and employed about 10-50 workers. They usually produced other farm machines, such as threshers and irrigation pipes in addition to tractors. Fourteen large firms produced more than 1,000 units annually and employed 50-200 workers. They were normally more vertically integrated, producing many parts and components themselves.

Most of the medium and large firms were located in the central region. Although the number of medium and large firms was increasing, the number of small ones was decreasing. All the firms were owned by Thais.

TFPG MEASUREMENT OF VARIABLES AND DATA SOURCES

Measurement of TFPG is based on an unrestricted, linear homogeneous, smooth, aggregate production function which allows substitution possibilities between all inputs. The inputs are categorized as labor, capital, and raw materials. The i-th firm's production at time t may be defined as:

$$Q_i(t) = f_i\left\{ L_i(t), K_i(t), M_i(t), t \right\} \tag{1}$$

where:

$Q_i(t)$ is real output of the i-th firm at time t,
$L_i(t)$ is labor employed by the i-th firm at time t,
$K_i(t)$ is physical capital used by the i-th firm at time t,
$M_i(t)$ is real intermediate inputs used by the i-th firm at time t,
t is a "shift" variable subject to time,

and the subscripts

$$i = 1, 2, \ldots, n \text{ and } t = 1, 2, \ldots, T.$$

Totally differentiating equation 1 with respect to time we obtain:

$$\frac{\hat{Q}_i(t)}{Q_i(t)} = f_{i, L_i}(t) \cdot \frac{L_i(t)}{Q_i(t)} \cdot \frac{\hat{L}_i(t)}{L_i(t)} + f_{i, K_i}(t) \cdot \frac{K_i(t)}{Q_i(t)} \cdot \frac{\hat{K}_i(t)}{K_i(t)}$$

$$+ f_{i, M_i}(t) \cdot \frac{M_i(t)}{Q_i(t)} \cdot \frac{\hat{M}_i(t)}{M_i(t)} + \frac{f_{i,t}(t)}{Q_i(t)} \tag{2}$$

where (^) denotes the rate of change of the variables over time.

Equation 2 shows that the rate of growth of real output can be decomposed into the weighted averages of the rates of growth of labor input, physical capital, and raw materials, where the weights are the output elasticities of the corresponding factors of production and the rate of growth of the shift variable.

Under competitive equilibrium, where each input is paid according to the value of its marginal product, equation 2 can be written as:

$$\frac{\hat{Q}_i(t)}{Q_i(t)} = \frac{w_i(t) L_i(t)}{P_i(t) Q_i(t)} \cdot \frac{\hat{L}_i(t)}{L_i(t)} + \frac{r_i(t) K_i(t)}{P_i(t) Q_i(t)} \cdot \frac{\hat{K}_i(t)}{K_i(t)} + \frac{P_i^m(t) M_i(t)}{P_i(t) Q_i(t)} \cdot \frac{\hat{M}_i(t)}{M_i(t)} + \frac{f_{i,t}(t)}{Q_i(t)} \tag{3}$$

where:

$w_i(t)$ is the nominal wage rate of the i-th firm at time t,

$r_i(t)$ is the nominal rental rate of capital of the i-th firm at time t,

$P_i^m(t)$ is the price of raw materials of the i-th firm at time t,

$P_i(t)$ is the price of products of the i-th firm at time t.

By letting α and β represent labor and raw material shares of the value of the i-th firm's total production, respectively, Euler's theorem, which assumes a linear homogeneous production function, implies that the capital share is $(1-\alpha-\beta)$, and equation 3 can be rewritten as:

$$\frac{\hat{Q}_i(t)}{Q_i(t)} = \alpha(t) \frac{\hat{L}_i(t)}{L_i(t)} + \left[1-\alpha(t)-\beta(t)\right] \frac{\hat{K}_i(t)}{K_i(t)} + \beta(t) \frac{\hat{M}_i(t)}{M_i(t)} + \frac{f_{i,t}(t)}{Q_i(t)} \tag{4}$$

Notice that, given these assumptions, the TFPG of the i-th firm can be measured from the following differential equation, or accounting identity, without estimating directly the production function or the output elasticities.

$$\frac{f_{i,t}(t)}{Q_i(t)} = \frac{\hat{Q}_i(t)}{Q_i(t)} - \left[\alpha(t) \frac{\hat{L}_i(t)}{L_i(t)} + \left\{1-\alpha(t)-\beta(t)\right\} \frac{\hat{K}_i(t)}{K_i(t)} + \beta(t) \frac{\hat{M}_i(t)}{M_i(t)}\right] \tag{5}$$

Estimation of TFPG of tractor firms from equation 5 requires measures of real output, real inputs, and shares of all factors of production for successive years. This is possible given the availability of annual data on units of production, values of intermediate inputs, numbers of workers, capital stock, and factor shares. Data were obtained from surveys and interviews of firms in the peak producing season, February to April 1980. Only medium and large firms were included in the surveys because small firms did not maintain records on inputs and output. Also, it would have been expensive to survey the small firms — they were too numerous and scattered throughout the country, while accounting for less than 15% of total production.

The initial year of production, yearly production, raw materials used, labor employed, and investment in structures, machinery, and equipment were recorded in the interviews. Most medium firms started production in the mid-1960s, half of the large firms started in the early 1970s. The latest year of records was 1979. Details of the survey and the methods of estimating all variables from these data are described below.

Physical output

The physical output of single-product firms was the number of tractors produced each year. For firms producing more than one product, the physical output was estimated by aggregating all products weighted by relative prices. The weighting procedure was as follows. Let

$Q_{ij}(t)$ be the units of the j-th product produced by the i-th firm at time t,

and

$P_{ij}(t)$ be the price of the j-th product of the i-th firm at time t,

where $i = 1, 2, \ldots, n, j = 1, 2, \ldots, l, \ldots, m$ and $t = 1, 2, \ldots, T$. The aggregate physical output of the i-th firm at time t, $Q_i(t)$, in terms of the l-th product can be written as:

$$Q_i(t) = \sum_{j=1}^{m} P_{ij}(t) \cdot \frac{Q_{ij}(t)}{P_{il}(t)} \qquad (6)$$

The continuous growth rate of physical output of time t, $q_i(t)$, is found by subtracting the logarithm of the output of the previous period from the logarithm of the output of the current output. That is:

$$Q_i(t) = \ln Q_i(t) - \ln Q_i(t-1). \qquad (7)$$

Real intermediate inputs

Intermediate inputs comprised raw materials, electricity, and fuel. The raw materials included sheet steel, steel rods, angle steel, chains, bearings, seals, gears, pulleys, steering sets, wheel rims, bolts, and nuts.

More than half of these were produced domestically. If the number of units of each of the raw materials used each year were available, they could have been aggregated using relative prices as weights in the same way as for physical output. Unfortunately, such data were available for only a few large firms and then only for 1979. No data were available for the medium firms; however, all firms could provide the total value of raw materials used each year. We therefore estimated the values of real intermediate inputs by disaggregating the total values in proportion to the value shares of the major purchased inputs. The major purchased inputs were defined as those accounting for at least 1% of total purchased inputs, subject to at least 90% of the value of purchased inputs. The value shares were computed from the 1975 input-ouput table, which is presently the only one available (NESDB 1980). Because the interviews indicated no major changes in purchased input coefficients and product composition over time, the 1975 value shares were applied to all years.

Real capital stock

Capital stock was classified into 1) buildings and structures, and 2) machinery, equipment, and vehicles. For each type in any year, real capital stock was obtained by adding current investment at constant prices to the real capital stock of previous year minus real depreciations accumulated up to that year.

That is, if we let

$K_{ik,t}$ be the real capital stock of the k-th type for the i-th firm at time t,

$I_{ik,t}$ be the investment flow of the k-th type of capital for the i-th firm at time t, evaluated at constant prices, and

δ_{ik} be the rate of replacement of the k-th type of capital stock by the i-th firm,

where $i = 1, 2, \ldots, n$, $k = 1, 2$, and $t = 0, 1, 2, \ldots, T$, then

$$K_{ik,t} = I_{ik,t} + (1-\delta_{ik})K_{ik,t-1}. \tag{8}$$

By a process of iterative substitution of $K_{ik,t-1}$

$$K_{ik,t} = (1-\delta)^t K_{ik,0} + \sum_{s=1}^{t} (1-\delta_{ik})^{t-s} I_{ik,t} \tag{9}$$

where $K_{ik,0}$ is the initial capital stock of the k-th type for the l-th firm.

For estimating real capital stock from equation 9, we need an estimate of initial real capital stock, flows of real investment, and rates of replacement. The initial real capital stock and annual real investment were obtained by deflating investment data from the surveys. The rate of replacement was defined as the reciprocal of the economic life of capital. The methods of measuring investment deflators and economic life of capital follow.

Investment deflators

Investment deflators were obtained from the Ministry of Commerce. The wholesale price indexes of construction materials were used for buildings and structures. The weighted averages of the indexes of machinery and equipment and transportation equipment were used for machinery, equipment, and vehicles. The weights were the value shares of total investment and amounted to about two-thirds for machinery and equipment and one-third for transportation.

Economic lives of assets

Buildings and structures are more durable than machinery and equipment. Krueger and Turner (1980) provide some estimates for Turkey. Assuming that structures, machinery, and equipment of Thai manufacturers have a life which is not significantly different from the Turkish, we have used an average structure life of 33 years and machinery and equipment life of 15 years.

Structure life was assumed to be invariant across industries, whereas machinery and equipment lives were made specific to each industry, based on estimates for U.S. industries (Park 1973). Because the average life of machinery and equipment in the U.S. is longer than in Thailand, Park's estimates were scaled down so that the weighted average for the entire manufacturing sector was 15 years.

Labor input

The labor input of a firm is the number of workers employed by that firm during the year. Initially, we intended to take account of quality differences. In the surveys, we asked firms to categorize the number of workers by sex, age, and education. After analyzing the data, we decided to use the total number of workers because there were no significant differences in labor quality among firms. Only one firm employed some female workers. Workers were from 15 to 50 years old. None had any formal education beyond high school and their skills were learned from working in machine shops. The proportions of workers by age and education did not vary much across firms.

Factor shares

The share of intermediate inputs was obtained for each year by dividing the value of intermediate inputs by the value of production. Labor shares were obtained likewise, where the value of labor was computed by multiplying the number of workers of each type by the corresponding wage rate, including adjustments for other benefits such as meals and lodging. The capital share was simply the residual.

ESTIMATING TFPG OF THE AGRICULTURAL MACHINERY INDUSTRY

Of the 30 firms interviewed only 14 (6 large and 8 medium) provided sufficiently complete and reliable data for estimating TFPG. Data were checked for reliability by comparing with reports of other financial and government institutions. Of the 14 firms, 6 were in the greater metropolitan area; the rest were in other major rice growing provinces in the central region: Ayuddhaya, Chachoengsao, and Nakorns-wan. Four of the 6 large firms were the major four-wheel tractor producers in the country, accounting for more than 85% of domestic production. The rest of the large firms and all of the medium firms produced 75% of the two-wheel power tillers and other farm machinery. Among the large firms, four started production after 1970 and two in the late 1960s. Among the medium firms, six started production after the mid-1960s and two in the mid-1970s.

Table 1 shows the average growth rates of output, input, and total factor productivity of the surveyed firms for three periods (initial year of production to 1970, 1970-76, and 1976-79) and also from the initial year of production to 1979. From the initial year to 1979, TFPG accounted for about 19% of the rate of growth of real output while 81% was from input growth. Output and employment grew faster in the first period when two-wheel tillers were newly introduced and in the second period when four-wheel tractors became more popular. During the second period, large

Table 1. Output, input, and productivity growth of all farm machinery firms.

Period	Growth rate per annum (%)			
	Output	Labor	Capital	Total factor productivity
Initial to 1970	34.94	23.21	9.67	5.91
1970-76	38.02	20.56	23.90	8.29
1976-79	13.23	6.18	11.69	2.10
Initial to 1979	28.02	13.81	18.96	5.33

rises in farm income, food prices, and wages occurred. Capital input increased much faster in 1970-76 due to the initial investment of some new large firms. TFPG from the initial year to 1976 was about 7%, accounting for about 10% of growth in real output. For the most recent period, TFPG was about 2%.

The growth rates of output, input, and total factor productivity of the large and the medium firms from the initial year to 1979; and for the three periods; are in Table 2. For the initial year to 1970, the sample consisted of two large and six medium firms. Output, labor, and capital of the large firms grew much faster than those of the medium ones, but TFPG was similar. During 1970-76, output and the TFPG of the medium firms increased substantially. However, the growth rate of employment for the large firms slowed down, but capital growth increased because of the entry of four new large firms. The TFPG of the large firms in this period was almost the same as in the previous one. During 1976-79, all firms showed a slowdown in the growth of output, inputs, and total factor productivity. However, the growth rate of capital of the medium firms was influenced by the entry of two new firms. For all periods, TFPG was higher for medium than large firms.

TFPG for all manufacturing industries, including machinery and equipment, is in Table 3. The industries were disaggregated in accordance with the three-digit International Standard Industrial Classification (ISIC) of manufacturing industries and the estimates of TFPG derived from secondary data for 1963-76. Details of the data sources and estimation procedures are given in Wiboonchutikula (1982). From Table 3, the TFPG of the machinery and equipment industry, which includes the manufacturers of all agricultural machines and equipment as well as other wood or metal working machines was −1.36. This is much lower than the TFPG estimated for the sample large and medium agricultural machinery firms during the same period. There are several possible reasons for the difference:

- The assumptions necessary for estimating TFPG may not be valid. It would therefore be unreasonable to expect consistent results. This could be investigated by relaxing some of the assumptions and reestimating TFPG.
- ISIC industry 382 includes a wider range of firms than medium and large-scale manufacturers of agricultural machinery. TFPG of these other firms may have been even more negative than that of the aggregate.
- The data were from firms still in business, and these we would expect to be the more successful. It is therefore likely that TFPG of the sample may have overestimated that of the population.

Table 2. Output, input, and productivity growth of large and medium farm machinery firms.

Period	Growth rate per annum (%)							
	Output		Labor		Capital		Total factor productivity	
	Large	Medium	Large	Medium	Large	Medium	Large	Medium
Initial to 1970	46.05	33.6	53.65	18.14	14.08	8.94	5.72	5.94
1970-76	40.05	36.86	20.73	20.46	36.40	16.76	5.74	9.63
1976-79	10.73	14.80	7.75	5.20	11.05	12.09	0.63	3.02
Initial to 1979	25.56	29.55	16.48	12.15	22.05	17.03	3.71	6.35

Table 3. The TFPG of 3-digit ISIC^a manufacturing industries, 1963-76.

ISIC industry	Material share	Labor share	Growth rate of			TFPG
			Output	Labor	Capital	
311 Food processing	.7137	.0511	12.16	9.41	8.41	1.25
312 Food products	.7984	.1022	25.26	21.25	20.91	−1.30
313 Beverages	.3329	.0690	16.02	12.20	12.50	1.38
314 Tobacco	.4318	.0520	6.82	3.04	3.33	1.44
321 Textiles	.5746	.1050	15.42	9.93	16.53	1.78
322 Wearing apparel	.5990	.1682	16.30	7.74	17.49	−0.37
323 Leather & leather products	.7210	.0717	16.30	14.16	13.72	1.98
324 Shoes	.6878	.1880	16.30	12.61	14.35	−1.06
331 Wood and cork	.6717	.1264	5.70	4.17	5.97	0.15
332 Furniture & Fixtures	.7015	.1013	16.30	11.85	16.95	−1.41
341 Paper & paper products	.6765	.1012	16.76	11.03	9.99	2.98
342 Printing & publishing	.5595	.1493	16.30	9.92	13.26	3.00
351 Basic chemicals	.5661	.0669	20.81	22.01	13.83	1.57
352 Chemical products	.6316	.0901	11.45	7.14	8.49	1.16
353 Rubber & rubber products	.6944	.0530	25.16	20.20	27.15	1.05
361 Nonmetallic minerals	.6241	.2658	29.00	25.07	28.58	−1.99
362 Glass & glass products	.4816	.1312	14.55	13.19	18.66	−2.99
369 Other nonmetallic	.7086	.0871	11.46	5.29	11.98	−1.36
371 Ferrous metals	.8308	.0609	17.37	14.76	17.33	0.04
372 Nonferrous metals	.5775	.0431	26.68	12.94	14.88	3.18
381 Metal products	.7059	.0655	1.29	0.25	5.49	−0.39
382 Machinery and equipment	.6431	.0589	16.30	9.22	17.93	−1.36
383 Electrical machinery	.6911	.0809	53.15	45.89	45.87	3.22
384 Transport equipment	.8151	.0618	20.18	14.28	18.68	−2.09
390 Miscellaneous	.6341	.0991	16.30	10.30	16.21	−0.32
Average	.6429	.0980	17.73	13.11	15.94	0.38

^{a}International Standard Industrial Classification.

Comparison of the aggregate estimate of TFPG for the machinery and equipment industry shows that it is well below the overall average for manufacturing industries; in fact, only four of the other industries had lower TFPG. This could be because the industry is relatively young and still developing. As yet, most agricultural machinery firms have been operated by workers without any formal training and who work with rather old or secondhand machines in plants with poor layouts. Training programs to upgrade the skills of workers, technical assistance at the plant level, and incentives to increase investments may help improve the total factor productivity of the industry.

REFERENCES CITED

Christensen, L. R., and D. W. Jorgenson. 1970. U. S. real output and real factor input, 1927-1967. Rev. Income and Wealth 16:19-50.

Denison, E. F. 1974. Accounting for United States economic growth 1929-1969. The Brookings Institution, Washington, D.C.

Jorgenson, D. W., and M. Ezaki. 1973. The measurement of macroeconomic performance in Japan, 1951-1968. In K. Ohkawa and Y. Hayami, eds. Economic growth: the Japanese experience since the Meiji era, Vol. 1, No. 19, Tokyo.

Kendrick, J. 1973. Postwar productivity trends in the United States, 1948-1969. National Bureau of Economic Research, New York.

Krueger, A. O., and B. Tuncer. 1980. Total factor productivity growth in Turkish manufacturing. University of Minnesota. (mimeo.)

NESDB (National Economic and Social Development Board), Institute of Developing Economies, and National Statistical Office of Thailand. 1980. Basic input-output table of Thailand, 1975, Bangkok.

Nishimizu, M., and C. R. Hulton. 1978. The sources of Japanese economic growth: 1955-1971. Rev. Econ. Stat. 351-361.

Park, W. R. 1973. Cost engineering analysis. John Wiley and Sons, New York.

Solow, R. M. 1957. Technical change and the aggregate production function. Rev. Econ. Stat. 312-320.

Thailand Ministry of Commerce, Price Index Division. Various years. Wholesale price indexes in Thailand. Bangkok.

Wiboonchutikula, P. 1982. The measurement and analysis of the total factor productivity growth of the manufacturing industries in Thailand. Ph D dissertation, University of Minnesota.

DOMESTIC RESOURCE COST OF AGRICULTURAL MECHANIZATION IN THAILAND: A CASE STUDY OF SMALL RICE FARMS IN SUPANBURI

S. Sukharomana

Farm mechanization, especially expansion of labor-displacing technologies for rice production, reduces the use of domestic resources and increases the demand for imported inputs such as fuel, oil, engines, and spare parts. The effects of farm mechanization on the domestic resource cost of earning a net unit of foreign exchange from rice production are less than the effects of yield and the opportunity cost of land. Mechanization has a tendency to generate profits for society even though the demand for imports of machinery-related items is increased.

There are two kinds of rice production technology — land augmenting and labor displacing. The first increases output without expansion of the area of farmland; the second reduces the requirement of labor per unit of farmland. Examples of land augmenting technologies are improved seeds, chemical fertilizers, insecticides, herbicides, fungicides, and improved cropping patterns. Labor-displacing technologies include tractors and threshers. Adoption of a new technology affects the use of domestic resources (land, labor, and domestic capital) directly and indirectly. These effects need to be identified and measured, because they may have implications for policies relating to resource utilization and allocation.

This study investigates the direct and indirect effects of farm mechanization and measures:

- the domestic resource and foreign exchange costs of machinery production and use; and
- the effects of farm mechanization on domestic resource and foreign costs of rice production, that is, the ratio of domestic resource cost to the net foreign exchange earned from rice production.

Economics Department, Kasetsart University.

METHODOLOGY

The first stage in measuring the domestic resource cost of mechanized rice production involves estimating the per unit social cost of production for each machine type and the social cost of-operating a machine or an animal for crop production. The marginal costs of undertaking farm activities using different machine types and intensities, such as land preparation by two-wheel and four-wheel tractors, or rice threshing by animal power, two-wheel tractor, or thresher, can then be estimated. The second stage measures the domestic resource cost per unit of net foreign exchange earned from rice production at different levels of farm mechanization.

The social cost of machine production and use

The social cost of machine production and use can be measured by estimating the costs of component inputs valued at their social prices. For primary or nontradable inputs (land, labor, and domestic capital), the social price was assumed to be the same as the market price. For imported and tradable inputs, the social prices were equated with their border values: c.i.f. if imported, and f.o.b. if exported. The social cost per unit is the sum of the social costs of the individual components. This can be written as:

$$SC_k = \sum_{i=2}^{n} p_i q_i + \sum_{j=n+1}^{m} p_j q_j \cdot SER \tag{1}$$

where:

p's are the social prices,
q's are the amounts,
SER is the shadow exchange rate (baht/dollar),
$i = 2, \ldots$, n refers to primary and nontradable inputs, and
$j = n + 1, \ldots$, m refers to the tradable inputs.

By convention the P_i's are measured in local currency and the P_j's are converted to local currency using the shadow exchange rate which reflects the tax structure on imports and exports (McCleary 1976).

Domestic resource cost of a unit of net foreign exchange earned

The domestic resource cost (DRC) of a unit of net foreign exchange earned is defined as the social cost of primary inputs used divided by the net foreign exchange earned. The net foreign exchange earned is defined as the difference between the border value of output and the value of tradable inputs at border price.

$$DRC = \frac{DC}{NF} = \frac{\sum\limits_{i=2}^{n} p_i q_i}{p_l q_l - \sum\limits_{j=n+1}^{m} p_j q_j \cdot SER} \tag{2}$$

where:

p_l = social price of output;
q_l = quantity produced; and
all other terms are as defined above

The DRC reflects a comparative advantage in rice production if its value is less than the shadow exchange rate (SER) (Akrasanee and Wattananukit 1976, Monke et al 1976, and Pearson et al 1976).

Since farm mechanization requires both imported capital input (engines) and imported operating inputs (fuel and spare parts), the quantity of foreign exchange used will increase with machine use. For a given yield, if an increase in machine use does not reduce the quantity of domestic resources used sufficiently to compensate for the DRC increase, production at that level of farm mechanization will be relatively inefficient. The effects of farm mechanization on DRC can be measured by the mechanization elasticity of DRC, defined as the percentage change in DRC resulting from a 1% change in mechanization.

DATA SOURCES AND THE LEVEL OF FARM MECHANIZATION

The primary data used for the analysis came from the farm record-keeping activity of the Thailand component of the Consequences of Mechanization project, 1979-80 wet season. The mechanization levels for the rainfed areas were animal only (A), animal and four-wheel large tractor (A+TL), animal combined with power tiller and tractor (A+PT+TL), and power tiller and tractor (PT+TL). The mechanization levels for the irrigated areas were (A+PT), (A+TS), (A+PT+TS), (PT+TS), (PT), and (TS), where TS indicates a small locally manufactured tractor. In the rainfed areas, large tractors were usually hired by the farmers for the first land preparation. In contrast, the tillers and locally manufactured four-wheel tractors used in the irrigated areas were owned by the farmers. Although observations for each mechanization category were few, the details collected should ensure accuracy.

Secondary data on tax and tariff rates, the cost structure of farm machine production, marketing, and transportation costs were collected from the reports of Customs Department, The Bank of Thailand, and National Economic and Social Development Board (NESDB).

Social cost of machine production

The engine is the major imported component of locally made machinery. The foreign cost of locally made machinery, at the border, ranged from 56 to 60% of production cost, whereas the primary factors used ranged from 33 to 39% (Tables 1, 2, and 3). For the imported large tractors, the share of foreign cost in the assembling cost was 83% and the primary input required for assembly was only 17%.

Table 1. Share of engine and body in the total value of locally made farm machines.

Type of machine	Engine (%)	Body and accessories (%)	Average investment cost	
			$	Year of estimate
Two-wheel tractor (PT)[a]	65	35	1020	1974-79
Small four-wheel tractor (TS)[a]	46	54	1540	1973-79
Rice thresher[b]	51	49	1072	1978
Water pump[a]	82	18	119.8	1973-79

[a]From farm record-keeping data, Supanburi Province, 1979-80 wet season. [b]Pathnopas (1980).

Table 2. Cost breakdown of machine body by type of locally made farm implement.

Item	Cost[a] ($)			
	Power tiller[b]	Local tractor[b]	Imported tractor[b]	Rice thresher[c]
Material cost				
Imported	41	32	83	41
Domestic	36	40	14	40
Direct labor cost	12	10	1	15
Electricity	5	5	0	2
Depreciation, interest, and taxes	7	13	2	2
Total	211	761	10000	748
Year	1978	1978	1978	1980

[a]Exchange rates, 1978 baht 20.25 = US$1, 1980 baht 20.40 = US$1. [b]Samahito and Kongkietngarm (1979). [c]Rungroj shop. A Rice Thresher Manufacturer in Chachoengsao Province, Thailand, April 1981.

Table 3. Primary and imported input components of farm machines.

Item	Components (%)				
	Two-wheel tractor	Small four-wheel tractor	Large tractor	Rice thresher	Water pump
Primary input[a] in					
Machine body and implement	19	33	na[b]	28	na
Engine	15	11	na	12	na
Subtotal (1)	34	44	17	40	21
Foreign cost					
Machine body and implement	14	18	na	20	na
Engine	46	32	na	36	na
Subtotal (2)	60	50	83	56	66
Taxes levied on					
Machine body and implement	2	3	na	1	na
Engine	4	3	na	3	na
Subtotal (3)	6	6	0	4	13

[a] Included all nonforeign costs of manufacturer. Costs of engine were calculated from the equation $uj = (1 + aj + tj + Tj) uj^*$. See Appendix 1. [b]na = not available.

Social cost of machine operation among mechanization methods

The social costs of farm mechanization for land preparation and rice threshing are in Tables 4 and 5. The social cost of land preparation by a two-wheel tractor is higher than that by a locally made four-wheel tractor because two-wheel tractors use more primary and tradable inputs. This is explained largely by the slower work rate of a two-wheel tractor while still requiring one man for operation, and the higher cost per hp for smaller engines. Land preparation by buffalo, costs more per hectare than land preparation by a two-wheel tractor, but no imported inputs are required (Table 4).

Because of the considerably lower use of domestic resources, the social cost of rice

Table 4. Social cost of alternative methods of land preparation, 1979-80 wet season, Supanburi, Thailand.

Item	Two-wheel tractor (baht/ha)	Small four-wheel tractor (baht/ha)	Buffalo (baht/ha)
Primary input			
Labor	56.13	28.06	168.38
Capital	57.37	24.55	–
Indirect labor and capital	22.33	16.63	60.00
Total primary input	135.83	69.21	228.38
Tradable input[a]	47.70	17.69	–
Taxes	19.50	10.00	–
Total	203.80	96.93	228.38

[a]Valued at shadow exchange rate: baht 23.44 = US$1. Source: Farm record keeping data, 1979-80 wet season.

Table 5. Social cost of alternative methods of threshing rice, Supanburi, Thailand, 1978 wet season.

Cost item	Thresher (baht/t)	Two-wheel tractor (baht/t)	Buffalo treading (baht/t)
Primary inputs			
Labor	35	97	180
Capital	15	19	–
Indirect labor and indirect capital	12	37	13
Total primary inputs	63	152	193
Tradable inputs[a]	27	34	–
Tax	1	3	–
Total costs	92	190	193

[a]Valued in baht at shadow exchange rate: baht 23.44 = US$1. Source: Pathnopas (1980).

threshing with a thresher is much lower than that with a two-wheel tractor or buffalo. The use of tradable inputs is also lower for the thresher. Threshers can save domestic resources, but they require imported fuel, oil, and an engine (Table 5).

DOMESTIC RESOURCE COST AND COMPARATIVE ADVANTAGE

The DRC coefficients of rice production in the rainfed areas were 26-75 baht/dollar, considerably higher than the 9.40-25 baht/dollar in the irrigated area (Table 6). The DRC coefficients for the rainfed areas were all greater than the SER as estimated by McCleary (1976), indicating no comparative advantage to rice production in these areas given the yields obtained in 1979-80.

The favorable coefficients for each category in the irrigated area resulted from the much higher yields obtained. Only power tiller users did not have a comparative advantage in rice production, and this group also had the lowest yield.

From Table 7, the elasticities of DRC with respect to tractor, rice thresher, and water pump use are positive, indicating that an increase in machine use will increase

Table 6. Domestic resource cost (DRC) for selected rainfed and irrigated rice production techniques in Supanburi, Thailand, 1979 wet season.

Water control	Level of mechanization[a]	Observations (no.)	Area (ha)	Yield (t/ha)	DRC (baht/$)	DRC/SER[b]
Rainfed	A	9	3.7	0.37	56.43	2.41
	A+PT+TL	3	5.9	0.46	75.08	3.20
	A+TL	3	4.1	1.19	31.08	1.33
	PT+TL	2	4.1	0.85	26.60	1.13
Irrigated	A+TL	5	3.0	2.68	16.90	0.72
	A+PT	2	2.5	3.84	13.61	0.58
	PT	6	4.0	1.89	25.23	1.08
	A+PT+TS	2	6.2	2.28	17.50	0.75
	TS	3	3.0	3.33	15.60	0.67
	PT+TS	2	5.6	6.25	9.64	0.41

[a] A = animal, PT = two-wheel tractor, TS = small four-wheel tractor, TL = large four-wheel tractor. [b] A shadow exchange rate (SER) of baht 23.44 = $1 was used for all calculations.

Table 7. Estimated input and output elasticities of domestic resource cost (DRC) coefficients, Supanburi, Thailand.[a]

Water control	Type of land preparation	DRC coefficients					
		Yield	Land	PT	T	Rice thresher	Water pump
Rainfed	A	−0.50	0.61	–	–	–	0.00
	A+PT+TL	−0.58	0.60	0.17	0.05	–	0.05
	A+TL	−0.30	0.52	–	0.14	–	0.01
	PT+TL	−0.44	0.62	0.30	0.0	–	0.01
Irrigated	A+TS	−0.33	0.44	–	0.04	0.02	0.0
	A+PT	−0.35	0.39	0.04	–	–	0.0
	PT	−0.44	0.51	0.17	–	0.02	–
	A+PT+TS	−0.40	0.50	0.00	0.03	–	–
	TS	−0.37	0.40	–	0.08	0.02	0.02
	PT+TS	−0.28	0.34	0.01	0.06	–	–

[a] A = animal, PT = two-wheel tractor, T = four-wheel tractor, WP = water pump, TL = large four-wheel tractor, TS = small four-wheel tractor.

the ratio of domestic resource to the net foreign exchange earned from rice production DRC. The elasticity with respect to farm mechanization, however, is less than that with respect to land.

Comparing the types of power used for land preparation, the mechanization elasticity of DRC was lower on irrigated farms which used small four-wheel tractors than on farms which employed two-wheel tractors. The main reasons appear to be the lower operating cost and the lower work hours per hectare of the small four-wheel tractor.

Where land preparation was done with a combination of tractor and animal power, the mechanization elasticity of DRC was less than where machines were used alone, regardless of whether the farm was irrigated or rainfed.

The negative sign of the yield elasticity of DRC indicates that an increase in yield will lower the DRC coefficient, whereas a yield reduction will increase the DRC coefficient. The elasticities, ranging between -0.30 and -0.58, imply that the yield effect on the DRC value is greater than the mechanization effect.

CONCLUSIONS

The best alternative methods were the locally made four-wheel tractor for land preparation and the thresher for harvesting. These reduced the use of both domestic and nondomestic resources.

The estimated elasticities indicate that farm mechanization affects the DRC coefficient value less than either yield or land does, because DRC elasticities with respect to the varied types of machine are less than those with respect to yield and land cost.

REFERENCES CITED

Akrasanee, N. , and A. Wattananukit. 1976. Comparative advantage in rice production in Thailand. Food Res. Inst. Stud. 15, 2.

McCleary, W. A. 1976. Equipment versus employment: a social cost benefit analysis of alternative techniques of feeder road construction in Thailand. International Labour Office, Geneva.

Monke, E., S. C. Pearson, and N. Akrasanee. 1976. Comparative advantage, government policies, and international trade in rice. Food Res. Inst. Stud. 15, 2.

Pathnopas, R. 1980. The economics of rice threshing machines in Thailand: a case study of Chachoengsao and Supanburi Provinces MS thesis, Faculty of Economics, Thammasat University, Bangkok.

Pearson, S. R., N. Akrasanee, and G. C. Nelson. 1976. Comparative advantage in rice production: a methodological introduction. Food Res. Inst. Stud. 15, 2.

Samahito, P., and K. Kongkietngarm. 1979. Report on farm machinery and farm equipment production: Part I. Farm tractor and power tillers. Bangkok: Industry Section, Economic Research Department, Bank of Thailand.

Appendix 1. Social value of output and tradable inputs.

I. Social value of output in 1979
    1) f.o.b. export price of 5% broken white rice   =   6.8136   B/kg
    2) farm price of paddy (1.5 kg of paddy = 1 kg
       white rice)   =   4.42   B/kg
    3) Export taxes   =   0.95   B/kg
    4) Processing cost, transportation cost and the
       profit of trader   =   1.4437   B/kg

Assuming that 20% of 1.4437 B/kg (or 0.289 B/kg) is the foreign cost and the rest was unallocated primary input.

II. Social value of tradable input
   Tradable inputs are seed fertilizer, insecticide, herbicide, fuel, and oil. Tradable inputs also include the tradable component of machine services.
   Rice seed was valued at the farm price. The following equation was used to calculate the border value of imported inputs:

$$U_j = (1 + a_j + t_j + T_j) U_j^*$$

where U_j is user's cost (value in baht at official exchange rate),
       a is added cost including wholesale retail and semi-processing cost,
       t is transportation rate,
       T is overall tax,
       U_j^* is border value of imported inputs (valued in baht at official exchange rate).

   In this study, a_j is given as the share of wholesale and retail value added to gross domestic product (GDP). The t_j is also assumed as the share of transportation and communication value added into GDP_j. In 1979 a_j and t_j were 24.36 and 7.65%, respectively. The imported content in transportation cost was small. The straight line method, assuming a 10-year machine life, was used to calculate machine depreciation. The average annual utilization of two-wheel four-wheel, and large tractors used in the calculations were 246, 360, and 1,000 hours, respectively. Annual utilization of rice threshers was set at 304 hours and that of water pumps at 300 hours.
   The overall tax (T) for each type of imported input was calculated from

$$T = t + b (1 + P) (1 + t) + mb (1 + P) (1 + t)$$
$$= t + b (1 + m) (1 + P) (1 + t)$$

where P = standard profit,
       t = tariff,
       b = business tax, and
       m = municipal tax.

   The tax rate of each import item was obtained from the Department of Customs, Ministry of Finance, Thailand (Tariff and Business Tax, 1977). Overall tax rates for each imported input are in Appendix 2.
   The primary and imported input components of farm machines used in the calculation of tradable and nontradable components for the depreciation of machines at users' costs are in Appendix 3. These included the added cost between the manufacturer and farmer. The shares of primary inputs are higher than in Table 3 which was calculated at the factory. Similarly, the share of foreign costs here is lower than in Table 3.

Appendix 2. Tax rates for imported agricultural inputs.

Import items	(t) Tariff	Tax rates (%)			
		(p) Standard profit	(b) Business tax	(m) Municipal tax	(T) Overall tax rate
Fertilizer	free	11.5	1.5	10	1.84
Insecticide	5%	11.5	1.5	10	6.84
Fungicide					
Herbicide					
Rodenticide					
(arsenic)	10%	8.5	1.5	10	11.97
Tractor with implements	free	16.0	8.0	10	3.83
Accessory input for tractor	free	26.0	3.0	10	4.158
Power engine	5%	13.0	3.0	10	8.915
Water pump complete set	15%	16.0	3.0	10	19.40
Accessory and spare parts for water pump	15%	26.0	3.0	10	19.78
Diesel oil	0.22 ฿ /1	value	0.7065 ฿ /1	10	1.30 ฿ /1
Gasoline oil	0.93 ฿ /1	value	3.045 ฿ /1	10	3.48 ฿ /1
Engine oil and lubricant	25 ฿ /1	value	0.30	10	25.45 ฿ /1

Appendix 3. Component shares for farm machines.

Cost item	Component share (%)				
	Two-wheel tractor	Small four-wheel tractor	Large tractor	Rice thresher	Water pump
Primary input in machine body and					
implements	23	38	na	34	na
engine	15	11	na	12	na
Subtotal (1)	38	49	37	46	21
Foreign cost in machine body and					
implements	11	13	na	15	na
engine	46	32	na	36	na
Subtotal (2)	57	45	63	51	66
Taxes levied on machine body and					
implement	1	2	na	na	na
engine	4	3	na	3	na
Subtotal (3)	5	5	0	3	13

CAUSES AND CONSEQUENCES OF POWER TILLER UTILIZATION IN TWO AREAS OF BANGLADESH

M. A. Jabbar, M. S. R. Bhuiyan, and A. K. M. Bari

Causes and consequences of power tiller utilization were examined using data collected from 63 tiller owners and 56 nonowners. Timely and quick cultivation, difficulty in managing large numbers of animals, low cost and better quality tillage, and animal shortage were the main reasons for purchasing tillers. Costs were low because of distortions in the prices of tillers and fuel. Unavailability of spare parts and lack of repair facilities were major problems. Tiller use increased size of cultivated holding, decreased regular labor, evicted tenants, changed tenure status, increased cropping intensity, and increased machine orientation of farmers. The findings indicated that mechanization of tillage would greatly benefit rich farmers at the expense of small and marginal ones.

The level of tillage mechanization in Bangladesh is quite low, with more than 98% of the land cultivated by bullock-drawn plows. There is, however, a growing shortage of power because long-term neglect of the livestock sector has resulted in decreased availability of bullocks. Use of mechanical power has not increased fast enough to fill the gap. The power gap, along with other factors, has probably been responsible for the slow growth of output and employment, and unless that gap is immediately filled, growth of agriculture might be further constrained (Jabbar 1980). The use of mechanical power has grown very slowly. Causes of the slow growth need to be identified and eliminated before any rapid increase can take place. The consequences also need to be measured for appropriate policy making.

A survey of power tiller owners and nonowners was conducted in two selected areas to:

- Identify the reasons for buying or not buying tillers;
- Study the characteristics of the tillers and the process of their acquisition and operation;
- Identify factors affecting the nature and extent of tiller use; and
- Measure the consequences of tiller use on selected aspects of the farm business, particularly 1) ownership of animal power, 2) ownership of land, 3) cultivation

Bangladesh Agricultural University.

of land, 4) tenure status, 5) cropping pattern and intensity, 6) employment of labor, and 7) machine orientation.

SELECTION OF AREA AND SAMPLE

Since the early sixties, 6,362 power tillers have been imported, of which 4,278 were reportedly sold to the private sector on highly subsidized credit provided through the Bangladesh Krishi Bank (BKB). The actual number and geographical distribution were not known but it was believed that operational tillers were scattered throughout the country, with a few small pockets of higher concentration. Mymensingh District and a cluster of four villages in Munshigonj Thana of Dacca District were selected as areas of low and high tiller density, respectively. The four Munshigonj villages were about 3 miles south of Munshigonj Thana headquarters. Mymensingh District covered over 10,000 km^2 while the 4 Munshigonj villages covered about 7.7 km^2.

Preliminary fieldwork revealed that a large number of tillers had been sold by the original owners, some to buyers outside Mymensingh. A large number of tillers had been out of operation for a number of years, and some operating tillers had been purchased from sources other than BKB. Complete enumeration showed 34 operational and 26 nonoperational tillers. Apparently, more than 150 tillers sold by BKB had been resold outside Mymensingh. Subsequent analyses were based on data collected from these tiller owners plus data from 26 nonowners located in the same villages.

Of the 29 operational tillers found in the four Munshigonj villages, 73% were in 1 village, South Char Masura. Data were collected from all 29 owners plus 22 nonowners on 3 visits to each farm.

REASONS FOR BUYING AND NOT BUYING TILLERS

Reasons for buying tillers

Tiller owners were asked their reasons for purchasing tillers. Nonowners were asked whether they were interested in buying and, if so, why. Fifty-six percent of nonowners in Mymensingh and 82% in Munshigonj expressed interest in buying tillers. The relative importance of the reasons varied among owners and intending owners and also between the two areas. In general, frequently stated reasons included increased output, reduced costs, and reduced drudgery (Table 1).

The implications of some of the responses need explanation. First, 30% of both owners and intending owners reported a shortage of animal power. Only 8% of intending owners mentioned labor saving. This supports recent findings of a significant shortage of animal power, which machines would overcome (Jabbar 1980).

Second, 67% of the owners and 24% of intending owners expected tiller cultivation to be cheaper. At market prices, bullock cultivation was found to be 3-5 times more expensive than tiller or tractor cultivation (GOP 1970, Lawrence 1970, Mian and Hussain 1975) because the overvalued currency underpriced both tillers and fuel by 40-50%. At real prices, tractor or tiller cultivation was found to be 2-3 times more expensive than bullock cultivation (Lawrence 1970). Such distorted markets encourage substitution of animals by machines even in situations where labor is still plentiful and cheap.

Table 1. Distribution of reported reasons for purchase and intended purchase of a tiller.

Reported reasons	Owners (%)		Intending owners (%)	
	Mymensingh	Munshigonj	Mymensingh	Munshigonj
Timely/quick cultivation by tiller	100	100	45	76
Animal management difficult	50	100	10	17
Cheaper cultivation by tiller	82	48	25	22
Better land preparation	50	14	55	17
Animal power shortage	15	48	30	28
Multiple uses of tiller	18	10	–	–
Tiller custom service	–	13	5	33
Available on credit	12	3	–	–
Good for puddling dry hard soil	6	3	–	–
Labor saving	–	–	–	–
High death rate of weak animals	–	–	10	–
Sample size	34	29	18	18

Third, it has been argued there is a technical limit to the optimum size of a farm using animal and human labor. One reason is the management problem. Seventy-three percent of the owners and 14% of the intending owners indicated they had difficulty managing a large number of animals. Large landholders generally cultivate land up to that technical limit and rent out any excess. But engine power was expected to, and did, induce more self-cultivation (Jabbar 1977, 1980).

Fourth, one-third of the intending owners, mostly in Munshigonj, wanted to buy a tiller so they could provide custom services. Custom operation was already booming in Munshigonj and intending buyers might have been influenced by the prospects.

Fifth, only 7% of the owners mentioned availability of credit as a cause for buying a tiller. Credit was available for purchase of all new tillers.

Reasons for not buying a tiller

The reasons nonowners did not buy a tiller are in Table 2. More than 50% of the nonowners were interested in buying when their neighbors bought, but they could not because of capital shortage or unavailability of tillers. Most nonowners not interested in a tiller were located in Mymensingh. Their primary reasons were related to repair and maintenance. Many of the current tiller owners already face this major problem.

Table 2. Distribution of nonowners' reported reasons for not purchasing a tractor.

Reported cause	All nonowners (%)		Unwilling nonowners (%)	
	Mymensingh	Munshigonj	Mymensingh	Munshigonj
Lack of capital	38	18	–	–
Not available	21	27	–	–
Could not manage to buy	–	14	–	–
Lack of knowledge or experience with machine	6	23	14	–
Had/have adequate bullocks	6	14	29	–
Operation, maintenance, repair problems	15	5	85	50
Did not like machine	12	5	–	–
Animal cheaper	6	5	36	50
Sample size	34	22	16	4

CHARACTERISTICS, PROCESS OF ACQUISITION, AND OPERATION OF TILLERS

Brand and capacity

Tillers were either received as grant aid or imported on credit from Japan. Of the sample, 48% were Yanmar, 40% Mitsubishi, and 6% Kubota and Isaki. However, 70% in Mymensingh were Mitsubishi and 83% in Munshigonj were Yanmar.

Tiller capacity was 6-10 hp. Ninety-two percent of the Mitsubishi tillers were 6-8 hp and 82% of the tillers in Mymensingh were 6-8 hp. In Munshigonj, 55% were 6-8 hp and 45% were 8-10 hp.

Additional equipment and tiller

In Mymensingh, 50% of the tillers were purchased with one or more attachment. Attachments reported were pump (25%), trolley (23%), hauler (6%), and furrower (6%). Nine percent of tillers were purchased without additional equipment, but the owners bought them later. In Munshigonj, only one tiller was purchased with a pump attachment and two other owners purchased threshing equipment later.

Most owners of tillers with no attachments wanted to buy and those with some wanted more. In Mymensingh, tiller owners wanted to buy a trolley (35%), pump (32%), hauler (24%), and equipment for threshing, seeding, and electric generation (12%). In Munshigonj, 34% wanted a trolley and 65% wanted a pump.

Source and time of purchase

The government first imported tillers for experimental purposes, but a few were subsequently sold to farmers. Later tillers were imported and distributed through the BKB and also through private dealers who generally sold on credit from BKB. During 1972-74, the Bangladesh Agricultural Development Corporation (BADC), the public corporation responsible for import and distribution of agricultural inputs, distributed tillers with BKB providing credit.

Acquisition dates suggest that tillers have been use longer in Mymensingh than Munshigonj. In Mymensingh, 32% of the tillers were purchased during 1963-68, 41% in 1969-74, and 27% in 1975-80. For Munshigonj, the corresponding figures were 7%, 24%, and 69%, respectively. Sources for purchase of tillers are in Table 3.

Secondhand purchases from other farmers have increased consistently. In Mymensingh, secondhand tillers were 44% compared to 55% in Munshigonj. Six percent were more than 6 years old at the time of purchase, 39% were 5-6 years old, and 39% were 3-4 years old. The main reasons for selling were repair, maintenance, and operational problems.

Tiller price and sources of capital

Tiller prices varied with time of purchase, machine condition, brand and capacity, number and type of accessories included, type of payment, and supply source. For new tillers brand and capacity and supply source had minimal effect. An index of average price by time of purchase, and tiller condition is in Table 4. Up to 1974, prices were quite low, and secondhand tillers were sometimes more expensive than new ones. After 1974, the price of new tillers increased about 300%, but prices of secondhand tillers remained fairly constant.

All tillers purchased on full cash were secondhand and those purchased on full credit were new. Although they were purchased from BKB, BADC, and private dealers, BKB provided the credit in all cases. With part cash payments, 38% of the price was paid in cash. Most tillers purchased with part cash were new and supplied

Table 3. Percentage of tillers purchased from different sources by period.[a]

Period	Sources (%) of supply			
	Dealer	BKB	Other farmers	Others[b]
1963-65	33	67	–	–
1966-68	50	40	10	–
1969-71	14	58	14	14
1972-74	7	7	29	57
1975-77	–	50	38	12
1978-80	10	19	71	–
All periods	16	31	38	15

[a]Source: Field survey 1980. [b]Include tiller mechanics, Foreign Voluntary Agency, and Bangladesh Agricultural Development Corporation.

Table 4. Index of average price by time of purchase and condition of tiller.

Period purchased	Index of av price			
	Mymensingh		Munshigonj	
	New	Used	New	Used
1963-65	1.00	–	–	–
1966-68	0.90	1.20	0.78	–
1969-71	1.00	–	1.06	1.51
1972-74	0.76	1.01	1.94	–
1975-77	4.23	0.68	4.24	2.00
1978-80	3.05	1.63	3.58	2.23

by BKB, BADC, or a private dealer with BKB credit. Most sellers of used tillers accepted part cash payment. In two cases, full cash payment was made by borrowing from private lenders. The interest rate for BKB credit increased from 5% in the mid-1960s to 10% in the late-1970s.

Of 36 owners purchasing with credit, 64% had repaid fully, 25% partially, 6% not at all, and 5% had not yet reached the repayment stage. The number of defaulters was similar in both areas, but those in Mymensingh had been defaulting longer, some since 1966.

Characteristics of tiller operators

Respondents were asked who operated the tiller during the survey year. In Mymensingh, 12% used only family members, 32% annual hired labor and family members, 35% only annual hired labor, 12% hired tiller drivers, and 9% hired tiller drivers and family members. In Munshigonj, 14% used only family members, 45% hired tiller drivers, and 41% hired tiller drivers along with family members.

Over 90% of the family members operating tillers in Mymensingh had some secondary education and 15% were high school graduates. In Munshigonj, more than 40% of family tiller operators had no formal education and none had above secondary education. In both places, few tiller operators from the other categories had any education; none were educated beyond primary level.

Nine percent of the tiller owners in Mymensingh and 35% in Munshigonj reported receiving no training in tiller operation and maintenance. They learned mostly from other tiller drivers. Those receiving training obtained it predominantly from sellers: 29% of owners in Mymensingh and 48% in Munshigonj reported that a member of the family, who was trained by the supplier, taught other family members and hired laborers.

Major and minor breakdowns

The number of major breakdowns of the tillers since acquisition is in Table 5. Breakdowns increased with the tiller age at the time of purchase. The main reasons given for breakdowns were overturning during operation, loose-fitting parts, irregular gasoline delivery, and excessive or insufficient oil use. No owners could specify the reason for the third and fourth major breakdowns and 54% could not name the cause of the first and second major breakdowns.

During 1978-80, 64, 23, and 13% of the owners reported doing 1 to 4, 5 to 8, and more than 8 minor repairs, respectively. Repair frequency was significantly higher in Munshigonj. Average repair costs for the 2 years were $24 in Mymensingh and $41 in Munshigonj, and 20 and 14 potential work days, respectively, were lost.

Table 5. Major breakdowns of tillers by region.

Breakdowns (no.)	Mymensingh (%)	Munshigonj (%)
0	29	52
1	35	28
2	27	17
3 and 4	9	3

Repair facilities

Service guarantees, ranging from 1 to 3 years, were assured for 79% of the new tillers purchased in Mymensingh and 56% in Munshigonj. No guarantee was available for used tillers. Of those with service guarantees, 59% reported receiving proper service, 14% did not require service, and 27% (located in Mymensingh) did not get service apparently because of problems with suppliers.

In Munshigonj, repair facilities were available within 8 km. In Mymensingh, 30% of owners reported that the nearest repair shop was more than 64 km away, 30% reported between 32 and 64 km, and the remainder reported between 8 and 32 km. Tillers usually had to be hauled to repair shops on trains, trucks, boats or bullock carts, and then most of the repair shops did not stock sufficient parts. Sometimes transportation was not possible and mechanics, who charged very high fees, were called.

Tiller problems

The main problems in tiller use were unavailability of spare parts, lack of repair facilities, high priced spare parts and fuel, and unavailability of pure diesel (Table 6).

EXTENT OF TILLER USE AND RELATED FACTORS

Information on the extent of tiller use was collected from the owners for 1976-77 to 1979-80. For 1979-80, data were collected for each operation whereas for the 3 other years, the limited records kept by the users were supplemented by their recollections. Annual use varied from 640 to 696 hours in Mymensingh and from 1,144 to 1,432 hours in Munshigonj. Detailed analysis is based on 1979-80 only.

Various characteristics of tiller users in Mymensingh and Munshigonj are in Table 7. In Mymensingh, only 38% of the owners provided custom services, compared to 97% in Munshigonj. Custom services accounted for 9% and 59% of total operations, respectively. Possible reasons for the lower level in custom services in Mymensingh are fewer repair services and large landowner concern about loss of status in the area.

Forty-eight percent of the owners in Munshigonj traveled 16-40 km, usually by boat to provide custom services and another 11% traveled 8-10 km. Farmers with

Table 6. Problems in tiller use reported by owners.

Problem	Mymensingh (%)	Munshigonj (%)	All areas (%)
Unavailability of spare parts	94	76	86
Frequent breakdown	38	17	29
Lack of repair facilities	41	14	29
High price of spare parts	35	3	21
High price of fuel	35	7	22
Unavailability of pure diesel	15	31	22
High charge for mechanics	6	3	5
Lack of training facility for repair work	3	–	2
Lack of efficient tiller driver	3	–	2

Table 7. Extent of tiller use in 1979-80.

Characteristics	Mymensingh		Munshigonj	
	Farms (%)	Hours/farm	Farms (%)	Hours/farm
Type of work				
Tillage only	62	496	100	1192
Tillage and other tasks	38	1008	–	–
Area cultivated (ha)				
Under 6.0	23	176	52	872
6.1-8.0	23	536	21	1448
8.1-10.0	15	864	14	1800
10.1-12.0	8	1864	3	1960
12.1 and over	31	824	10	1224
Type of family				
Single	68	568	56	1088
Joint	32	976	44	1328
Past experience in machine use				
Yes	53	864	27	1304
No	47	424	73	1152
Main income source				
Farming	47	504	35	1352
Farming and business	44	752	62	1096
Farming and service	9	960	3	1400

inadequate, or no, draft animals bought tiller services. Twenty-four percent of the owners reported charging lower custom rates in distant places, but still making a profit because custom services were done after finishing their own work.

Tiller use increased with size of cultivated holdings up to 12 ha and then declined sharply. This size effect was indirectly reflected through type of family because most joint families had larger holdings.

Owners with experience in handling different types of machines used the tiller longer than those without such experience. Experienced owners could do minor repairs, getting more use from the tiller. In Mymensingh, owners who had income from business or services as well as farming had better external contacts which helped them locate mechanics, manage parts, and make quick repairs.

CONSEQUENCES OF TILLER USE

There are three approaches to measuring the effects of tiller use. First, tiller owners and nonowners may be compared at a given time with differences attributed to tiller use. The main problem with this approach is that owners and nonowners may differ in respects unrelated to tiller ownership. The second approach involves before-and-after comparison, with any differences attributed to the tiller. Here the main problems are that other changes might have taken place simultaneously and "before" data must be collected by recall, which is less reliable. The third possibility is to combine the cross section and time series approaches (Binswanger 1978). All three approaches were used in this study.

Effect on animal ownership

Tiller ownership was expected to have an immediate effects on work animal ownership. Changes in the number of owned work animals and the number per cultivated hectare are in Table 8. On the average, 2-2.5 animals were replaced by a power tiller. The degree of substitution was much higher in Munshigonj where 53% of tiller owners completely replaced their animals. Although only 3% of the farms in Mymensingh replaced all their animals, some of the larger ones replaced 5 or 6, yet still retained several because: 1) the tiller was not considered fully reliable, 2) the tiller was not suitable for puddling in low-lying areas or for preparing dry hard soils in summer, 3) land preparation with a tiller followed by laddering with animals gave better results, 4) during short sowing or planting seasons some larger farmers needed to supplement their tiller power with draft animals, 5) some farmers had increased their operational holdings beyond the capacity of one tiller, and 6) animals were fed mostly on crop by-products and could be retained for investment at little additional cost.

Effect on land ownership and tenure

Those who bought tillers in both areas normally had larger forms than those who did not (Table 9). By 1979-80, the farms in all categories were significantly larger, but the relative differences between owners and nonowners remained similar. Indeed, a substantial proportion of farmers had acquired additional land whether they had tillers or not. Tenure status of tiller owners and nonowners in both areas changed substantially. However, the impact of the tiller on and changes could not be ascertained.

Table 8. Changes in work animal ownership on farms of tiller owners and nonowners.

	Mymensingh		Munshigonj	
	Owner	Nonowner	Owner	Nonowner
Number of animals/farm				
Before tiller purchase	7.3	6.4	3.6	3.1
1979-80	5.3	6.8	1.1	2.4
% change	−27	+6	−70	−23
Number of animals per cultivated ha				
Before tiller purchase	0.22	0.20	0.17	0.19
1979-80	0.11	0.19	0.05	0.13
% change	−48	−8	−69	−33

Table 9. Changes in size of land ownership of tiller owners and nonowners.

	Land ownership			
	Mymensingh		Munshigonj	
	Owner	Nonowner	Owner	Nonowner
Year before tiller purchase (ha)	8.64	6.23	3.15	2.70
1979-80 (ha)	9.53	7.10	3.87	3.36
% change	10	14	23	25

Effect on cultivated area

There were negligible differences in the average size of cultivated holdings of tiller owners and nonowners in both areas at time of purchase (Table 10). By 1979-80, the average size of cultivated holdings of tiller owners and nonowners had increased in both areas. The difference between the two groups increased in Mymensingh but not in Munshigonj.

Regardless of tiller ownership, most farmers increased their areas under cultivation, and the predominant mechanism was acquiring new land (Table 11). Tiller owners in Mymensingh also increased their cultivated holdings by using land previously rented out or left fallow. Previously rented out land was used by 81% of tiller owners in Mymensingh, compared to only 33% in Munshigonj.

Effect on cropping pattern and intensity

Because farmers could not be expected to recall crop areas accurately over several years, cropping pattern and cropping intensity differences of the two groups were compared using average cropping patterns for 1978-79 and 1979-80. The proportions of irrigated crop area and of area devoted to high-yielding varieties (HYV) were similar for owners and nonowners in both areas. However, contrary to the findings of Gill (1979, 1980), cropping intensity differed markedly between the two groups in Munshigonj. It is likely that the increase in cultivated area in Mymensingh and in cropping intensity in Munshigonj was the result of different initial sizes of holdings.

The increased cropping intensity in Mushigonj was accompanied by greater diversification. A decrease in the paddy area on farms with tillers was accompanied by increases in the areas for potato, jute, mustard, and wheat.

Table 10. Changes in sizes of cultivated holdings of tiller owners and nonowners.

| | Cultivated holdings | | | |
| | Mymensingh | | Munshigonj | |
	Owner	Nonowner	Owner	Nonowner
Year before tiller purchase (ha)	4.75	4.80	2.92	2.63
1979-80 (ha)	7.59	5.95	3.61	3.11
% change	60	24	24	18

Table 11. Sources of additional cultivated land.

| | Additional cultivated land (ha) | | | |
| Source of land | Mymensingh | | Munshigonj | |
	Owner	Nonowner	Owner	Nonowner
New land acquired	0.89	0.87	0.72	0.66
Cultivation of previously rented out land	1.42	0.35	−0.08	−0.19
Cultivation of previously fallow land	0.60	−0.06	–	–
Mortgaged land	−0.03	−0.01	0.05	
Total additional land cultivated	2.84	1.15	0.69	0.48

Table 12. Changes in regular hired labor employment by tiller owners.

Location, time period	Hired labor/farm							Total no./culti-vated ha
	Annual plowman	Seasonal plowman	Other annual labor		Tiller driver	Tenant farmer	Total	
			Male	Female				
Mymensingh								
Before tiller purchase (no.)	2.15	0.79	3.90[a]	0.90[a]	—	7.00	14.74	3.11
1979-80 (no.)	1.68	0.38	3.60[a]	1.00[a]	0.20	3.00	9.86	1.31
% change	-22	-41	-8	+11	$+\infty$	-57	-33	-58
Munshigonj								
Before tiller purchase (no.)	0.66	0.31	0.90	0.30	—	2.00	4.17	1.43
1979-80 (no.)	0.28	0.14	0.60	0.30	0.86	2.00	4.18	1.14
% change	-59	-55	-33	—	$+\infty$	—	—	-21

[a] About 20% below 14 years old.

Effect on employment

Although the introduction of tillers may have various effects on employment, the only one measured was the effect on regular hired labor. This was done using a before-and-after comparison (Table 12). In Mymensingh, there was a negative, aggregate impact on regular employment per farm; in Munshigonj, employment per farm remained constant. In both areas, however, use of regular labor per hectare declined.

Most of the evicted plowmen were working as casual laborers on the same farms or elsewhere, and some got plowing jobs elsewhere. About 60% of the evicted tenants in Mymensingh were cultivating their own small holdings, or renting. Others became day laborers.

Tiller use has changed the pattern of family labor participation in farming. For example, the number of families having members working as plow drivers declined from 12% to 3% in Mymensingh and from 45% to 21% in Munshigonj following tiller introduction. On the other hand, 54% of the families had members working as tiller drivers in 1979-80. Other changes included increases in the number of family members participating in farm activities, hours worked per person, and increase in supervisory work.

Effect on machine orientation

After purchasing tillers, owners wanted to buy more equipment. However, lack of money and available machinery limited additional purchases. Although most desired machines are labor displacing, some have potential for indirect employment expansion.

CONCLUSIONS

Machine use is being encouraged by distorting market prices in a situation where animals are in short supply, but labor remains quite cheap. Such policies may be justified if tiller use increases output, but there is little supporting evidence. The large scale introduction of tillers appears likely to benefit the rich farmers, at the expense of small and marginal ones, through employment, tenancy, land accumulation, and machine orientation. Detailed studies, incorporating mechanization of other farm operations, are required if there are to be sound farm mechanization policies.

REFERENCES CITED

Binswanger, H. P. 1978. The economics of tractor in South Asia. Agricultural Development Council, Inc., New York, and International Crops Research Institute for the Semi-Arid Tropics, Hyderabad. 96 p.

Gill, J. 1979. Appropriate technology: mechanized land preparation. The ADAB News 6(12):22-23.

Gill, J. 1980. Appropriate technology: mechanized land preparation. The ADAB News 7(1):18-19.

GOP (Government of Pakistan). 1970. Farm mechanization in East Pakistan: report of the Farm Mechanization Committee. Islamabad, Pakistan. 225 p.

Jabbar, M. A. 1977. Relative productive efficiency of different tenure classes in selected areas of Bangladesh. Bangladesh Dev. Stud. 5(1):17-50.

Jabbar, M. A. 1980. Draft power shortage and mechanization of tillage in Bangladesh. Bangladesh J. Agric. Econ. 3(1):1-26.

Lawrence, R. 1970. Some economic aspects of farm mechanization in Pakistan. 61 p. (mimeo.)

Mian, M., and M. K. Hussain. 1975. A comparative study of the economics of cultivation by bullock and power tiller in the production of transplanted aman paddy in some selected areas of Bangladesh. Prod. Econ. and Farm Manage. Res. Rep. 1. Department of Agricultural Economics, Bangladesh Agricultural University, Mymensingh. 62 p.

ECONOMIC, TECHNICAL, AND SOCIAL ASPECTS OF TRACTOR OPERATION AND USE IN SOUTH SULAWESI, INDONESIA

J. Hafsah and R. H. Bernsten

Minitractors have been introduced into the relatively sparsely populated province of South Sulawesi to provide additional land preparation power. To better understand the impact of this program, 50 individuals in Sidrap and Pinrang Districts were interviewed. Ten of them bought minitractors in 1975-79. Information about socioeconomic characteristics and various aspects of tractor operations was collected. Analysis showed that tractor ownership was not economically viable because of breakdowns and a shorter than expected useful life. Utilization of new tractors during the first year has declined each year since 1975. This suggests that increases in the tractor population have made it more difficult for owners to cover variable and fixed costs.

Because rice is the staple food of Indonesia, government policy has focused on increasing production to achieve self-sufficiency. During the first five-year development plans (Pelita I 1969-74, and Pelita II 1974-79), rice output increased 4.7 and 3.8%/year, respectively. Yet, with population growing at 2.5%/year and incomes rising, demand still exceeds domestic supply (B. P. S. 1980).

Minitractors have been introduced into several places in the less densely populated outer islands in an effort to increase production and to remedy apparent shortages of human and animal labor. These shortages constrain area expansion, crop intensification, and synchronized rice planting.

In the first tractor feasibility study in South Sulawesi, Parussengi (1972) concluded there was a need for small tractors, because of a labor shortage. Follow-up studies by Gadjah Mada University and the Agricultural Equipment Office evaluated tractor needs in 18 of the 23 districts in South Sulawesi (Gadjah Mada University 1976, Directorate of Food Crops 1975, Agricultural Extension Service 1976, Directorate for Technical Agriculture 1979). Based on these studies, four-wheel minitractors were introduced to several districts beginning in the mid-1970s. By 1980, almost 1,300 minitractors had been sold throughout the province (Agricultural Extension Service 1980).

South Sulawesi Extension Service and Central Research Institute for Food Crops/IRRI Cooperative Program, Bogor, Indonesia.

Farmers in Sidrap and Pinrang first purchased minitractors in 1969. In 1975, a major government-sponsored program, aimed at increasing productivity, provided for considerably more tractors. An understanding of the successes and weaknesses of this effort should provide guidance for planning and implementing future tractor programs.

This study focuses on:

- the characteristics of minitractor owners and their reasons for purchasing;
- minitractor use;
- problems encountered in ownership, operation, and maintenance;
- financial arrangements and credit characteristics;
- the characteristics of tractor operators; and
- the profitability of tractor ownership.

METHODOLOGY

Sidrap and Pinrang Districts are about 180 km north of Ujung Pandang, the provincial capital of South Sulawesi. This is a highly productive agricultural area and has a population density of 93 persons/km² (B. P. S. 1980). Seventy percent of the 92,581 ha of lowland is irrigated, mostly by a modern technical system receiving water from the Saddang diversion dam (Agricultural Extension Service 1980). Typically, two irrigated crops are grown with farmers using the latest varieties along with fertilizer and insecticides.

Sidrap and Pinrang were chosen as the study area because these districts have the most minitractors. Four villages with the largest number were selected from each district. Of the 508 minitractors in the two districts in 1979, 108 were owned by residents of these eight villages. A few adopters bought units before 1976; however, most purchases (40%) were made in 1979 when Presidential Aid (BANPRES) was extended through the small investment credit system (KIK). Before the BANPRES program almost all purchases were Kubota, but in 1979 Iseki and Sateh captured 64% of the market.

Ten tractor owners, who purchased units in each of the previous five years, were randomly selected and interviewed once during each of the 1979 wet and 1979-80 dry seasons.

RESULTS

Characteristics of the sample farmers

Some characteristics of the 50 minitractor owners are shown in Table 1. Over 60% were between 31 and 50 years old and only 26% had education beyond primary school. Their principal occupation was farming (56%). Their average assets were 7.2 ha of riceland, valued at $17,120, and 3.1 cows and 0.7 buffalo, together valued at $520. The average value of all assets, excluding house and tractor, was $22,080.

By comparison, nonmechanized respondents in the same area had a similar age and education, but only 1.34 ha of riceland (Consequences Team 1981).

Respondents gave several reasons for purchasing a tractor (Table 2). Because most were large landowners, the most common answer was expected to be "to

Table 1. Characteristics of 50 minitractor owner respondents.

Characteristic	Number
Age (yr)	
≤ 30	0
31-40	15
41-50	16
> 50	14
Education (yr)	
Illiterate	14
Primary school	23
Junior/senior high school	7
University	6
Occupation	
Farmer	28
Government employee	7
Trader	10
Merit/service	5

Table 2. Reasons given by 50 minitractor owners for purchasing a tractor.

Reason	Responses[a] (no.)
To cultivate their land	71
To rent to neighbors	40
To experiment	12
Social prestige	9
Available credit	26
	158

[a]Some respondents gave more than one answer.

cultivate their own land." However, 25% expected to earn money renting the tractor to neighboring farmers, especially when pressed to meet repayments.

The respondents perceived several benefits from owning a minitractor (Table 3). Most important was the potential for timely planting, whereas only 10% mentioned increased yields and 8% reduced drudgery.

Minitractor characteristics

All the minitractors surveyed were rated at 12-15 hp and had diesel engines. Their costs which increased significantly over the period, averaged $5,513 (Table 4). These dollar prices understate the real rate of increase. With the 50% devaluation of the rupiah in November 1978, the price of a tractor to the Indonesian farmer in 1979 was 32% higher than in 1978.

In both wet and dry seasons, complete land preparation involved rototilling the field twice. However, some farmers hired the minitractor for only one rototilling then harrowed the field using animal or human power. Consequently, data on land preparation were converted into two rototilling equivalents. The hectares prepared each season since tractor purchase are shown in Table 5. For each purchase year, utilization was highest in the first year and declined in each successive year. At the

Table 3. Minitractor owners' perceptions of benefits associated with tractor ownership.

Reason	Farmers (no.)
Timely planting	45
Better land preparation	39
Reduced need to hire labor	39
Increased yields	15
Reduced drudgery	12

Table 4. Purchase price of sample tractors by year of purchase.

Purchase year	Purchase price ($)	Price index
1975	4471	100
1976	4941	111
1977	5647	126
1978	6588	147
1979	5920[a]	132
Mean	5513	

[a] Dollar price affected by devaluation from $1 = Rp425 to $1 = Rp625.

Table 5. Hectares plowed each season, by year of tractor purchase.[a]

Year, season	Area plowed (ha)				
	1975	1976	1977	1978	1979
1975					
Wet	55.5	–	–	–	–
Dry	46.6				
	102.1				
1976					
Wet	36.8	58.0	–	–	–
Dry	28.9	42.1			
	65.7	100.1			
1977					
Wet	30.5	34.9	43.6	–	–
Dry	25.7	34.3	29.8		
	56.2	69.2	73.4		
1978					
Wet	25.4	35.3	39.6	43.6	–
Dry	15.8	22.0	16.2	37.7	
	41.2	57.3	55.8	81.3	
1979					
Wet	10.3	20.8	20.5	24.6	33.9
Dry	3.9	7.8	10.8	16.5	23.3
	14.2	28.6	31.3	41.1	57.2
Average	55.9	63.8	53.5	61.2	57.2

[a] Average of hectares plowed by all units operating in respective seasons.

same time, it is clear that late adopters were unable to achieve the same use in the first year as early adopters, suggesting the tractor population may be reaching saturation.

The hectares prepared each year were distributed evenly between seasons, with 55-60% of the area plowed in the wet season, when tractors are used on both rainfed and irrigated land.

The relationship between tractor age and number of seasons it was broken is shown in Table 6. Reasons for not repairing the tractor were spare part unavailability, repair expense, or the repair cost equaling that of a new unit. Of 10 tractors

Table 6. Number of seasons during which minitractors operated.

Purchase year	Av season operating per tractor			Tractors (no.) operating in 1979-80 dry season	Av area plowed in 1979[b] (ha)
	Potential[a] (no.)	Actual (no.)	Seasons broken (%)		
1975	9.1	7.3	20	3	14.2
1976	7.3	6.6	10	5	28.6
1977	5.9	5.5	7	7	31.3
1978	3.0	2.9	3	10	41.1
1979	1.9	1.9	0	10	57.2

[a]The potential number of seasons the tractor could be used takes into consideration that some tractors were purchased after the beginning of a season and not used that season. [b]By units still operating in 1979.

Table 7. Damage requiring spare parts, reported by 50 tractor owners.

Part repaired or replaced	Units (no.) experiencing problem
Engine	
Injector	1
Piston	19
Dynamo	4
	24
Transmission	
Brake	5
Joint	7
Chain	7
Gears	10
Clutch	6
	35
Hydraulic	
Ring	1
Pump	2
Oil cylinder	2
	5
Implement	
Joint	3
Rotary blade	11
Floating wheel	2
	16

purchased in 1975, only 3 were still operating in 1979 and they averaged only 14.2 ha. The data in Table 6 suggest that minitractors are relatively free from major problems for the first 2 years, but thereafter use is reduced significantly. It appears that the maximum useful life of minitractors is 5 years. As shown in Table 7, breakdowns were most frequently associated with the transmission (43%). The parts requiring replacement most often were the piston (23%) and associated components. Transmission damage was probably aggravated by erratic stopping and starting, engine damage from late oil changes, and continuous operating beyond the recommended hours per day. These explanations are consistent with the owners' observations (Table 8). Breakdowns might be greatly reduced through better driver training and supervision.

Respondents felt that spare parts were expensive and 43% reported they were not always available when needed. Other reasons for delays in repairs are in Table 9.

Financial arrangements and credit characteristics

Ninety-four percent of the minitractors were purchased on credit — 74% from banks, and 20% from dealers. Credit purchases were made easier by the BANPRES program, extending the payback period to 72 months, providing a low interest rate of 10.5%/year, and reducing the land required for collateral from 5 to 2.5 ha (Team on Selective Mechanization 1979). Sole owners accounted for 81% of the tractor purchases.

Arrears on minitractor loans varied by year of purchase. At the end of the 1979 dry season, loan defaults were 0% for 1975 purchases, 12% for 1976, 5.4% for 1977, 15% for 1978, and 4% for 1979. The most important reasons for difficulties in meeting loan payments are in Table 10.

Table 8. Perceptions of 50 owners as to causes of damage to their units.

Reason	Respondents[a] (no.)
Poor maintenance	32
Improper driving	19
Driver turnover	18
Distance from workshop	8
Low quality equipment	7
Poor quality workshop service	4
	88

[a] Some respondents gave more than one answer.

Table 9. Reasons for delays in repairing broken units.

Reason	Respondents (%)
Spare parts not available	43
Distance from workshop	24
No time to bring minitractor to workshop	20
No money to pay for repairs	13

Minitractor operators

Because the tractor operator is a key to the length of service life, the 70 operators were interviewed. Generally, operators were younger and more educated than the owners (Table 11). About 59% were sons of the owners, 37% relatives, and only 14% from outside the family. Slightly more than 50% of the operators had no other occupation. Of those with second jobs, 88% operated their own farm. Most operators had very little driving experience and training appeared to be inadequate (Table 11). The few organized training courses had been sponsored by dealers (63%), the government (25%), and jointly (12%). Of the 12 operators who had attended a course, 5 were taught only driving, 3 only maintenance, and 4 both. Although dealers agreed to provide training for new owners, few owners operated the units themselves and they had insufficient knowledge for training the actual operators.

Table 10. Reasons given by 50 minitractor owners for having difficulties in repaying their tractor loans.

Reason	Respondents[a] (no.)
Minitractor damaged	45
Cannot plow enough area	30
Crop failure	12
Renters do not pay	9
Used for other purposes	6
	102

[a]Some owners gave more than one reason.

Table 11. Characteristics of 70 minitractor operators.

Characteristic	Number
Age (yr)	
15 - 30	60
21 - 25	23
Formal education (yr)	
0	8
1 - 6	48
> 6	14
	70
Driving experience (yr)	
1 - 2	45
3 - 4	21
> 4	2
	68
Training courses	
0	58
1	11
2	1
	70

The most frequent reasons individuals chose tractor driving were increased prestige, supplemental income, and job satisfaction (Table 12). Abbas (1977) noted that operators regarded driving a tractor similar to driving a car, in that they can listen to the radio while working and it gives them "style."

Operators earn a high income generally 15-20% of the plowing rate. In addition, the landowner provides snacks and cigarettes to encourage good work. If 30 ha are cultivated, at $40/ha, the operator's share would be $180-240 for the 60-day land preparation season. This is a daily wage of $3-4 with meals, compared to a bricklayer's or carpenter's $1.20-2.40/day without meals.

Custom activities

The land preparation charge is established jointly by the tractor owners and the Extension Service each year, although some owners charge less than the agreed rates to increase demand. The average annual increase in custom rates between 1975 and 1979 has been 33%. About 86% of the area plowed has been custom work for local farmers but some owners traveled as far as 50 km.

ECONOMIC EVALUATION

Data collected from each minitractor owner were costs and returns for each season he operated the tractor.

In November 1978 , the Indonesian rupiah was devalued from Rp 425 to Rp 625 to the dollar. To simplify interpretation, all results are presented in dollars using the current exchange rate of $1 = Rp 625.

Table 12. Economic analysis of minitractors by year of purchase.

Item	1975	1976	1977	1978	1979
Av area plowed (ha/yr)	58.9	63.8	53.5	61.2	57.2
Capital investment ($)	3040	3360	3840	4640	5920
Average fixed costs					
Depreciation ($)	547	605	691	828	1066
Interest ($)	219	282	369	497	710
Total ($)	766	887	1060	1325	1776
Average variable costs $/ha	7.56	7.96	9.89	10.72	11.57
Average gross revenue $/ha	19.24	23.27	26.66	31.02	38.35
Break-even area (ha/yr)	65.6	57.9	63.2	65.3	66.3
Annual cash flows ($)[a]					
1974	−3040	−	−	−	−
1975	860	−3360	−	−	−
1976	758	1289	−3840	−	−
1977	761	−1051	1097	−4640	−
1978	595	961	936	1463	−5920
1979[b]	595	1547	2425	3991	6386
Benefit-cost ratio[b]	0.91	1.06	0.92	0.98	0.97
Net present value ($)[b]	−412	296	−388	−109	−218

[a]For computational purposes, capital investments are assumed to be made at the end of year 0, that is the year before the tractor was actually purchased. [b]Estimated using a discount rate of 12%.

For breakeven point analysis, annual fixed costs were computed as depreciation plus interest. Annual depreciation was calculated as initial cost less salvage value divided by the useful life of 5 years. Salvage value was assumed to be 10% of the initial cash price. Interest was calculated at 12%/year on the declining unpaid balance and averaged over the 5-year life. Because the price of minitractors increased each year, total fixed costs have also risen for tractors bought each successive year.

Variable costs included all expenditures on fuel, oil, repair and maintenance, and the driver's salary. These costs increased each year for all tractors, partly due to increases in the price of inputs and increases in the repair and maintenance component as tractors aged. In 1979, the variable costs per hectare for new tractors were 30% less than for tractors purchased in 1975.

Gross revenue was estimated as the custom operation rate multiplied by the total area plowed (custom work and own land). This formula assumes that the shadow price of own land preparation is the same as the cost for custom operation. Although gross revenue per hectare increased each year as the contract rate rose, gross revenue per season declined due to falling utilization as the tractor aged. Gross revenue and variable costs were converted to a per-hectare basis by dividing the total value over the years of use by the total area prepared. With these data, it was possible to compute the average break-even area to be prepared per annum over tractor life and compare this with actual tractor performance. Benefit-cost (B:C) ratios for each purchase year could also be estimated by discounting the cash flows.

Values used for estimation and results of the break-even and B:R analyses are shown in Table 12. In only one case (tractors purchased in 1976) was the average annual use larger than the break-even use. Similarly, 1976 was the only year of purchase for which (using a discount rate of 12%) the B:C was greater than unity and the net present value (NPV) was positive. Increasing the discount rate to 15% did not alter these conclusions. However, in each of the other years, the B:C was close to unity.

When estimating these results, all capital investments were assumed to be made at the end of the year before operation started. Although this makes no difference if the tractor was actually purchased at the beginning of the wet season, it will underestimate the B:C and NPV for later purchases. Computations were based on cost and return data for all tractors operating during the respective years. Yet, 1978 tractors did not operate in 3% of the season following purchase, 1977 models in 7%, 1976 models in 10%, and 1975 models in 20% (Table 6). Consequently, if seasons during which tractors were inoperable were taken into consideration, the B:C and NPV would be lower than in Table 12. In addition, the computation of B:C and NPV was influenced by the fact that only those tractors purchased in 1975 had been fully depreciated. The salvage values used for tractors purchased in other years were the depreciated values.

CONCLUSIONS

Minitractors have been used in Sidrap and Pinrang Districts for several years. Evaluation of data collected from 10 owners who purchased minitractors from 1975 through 1979 showed that, even when purchased with subsidized credit, these tractors were not economically viable. Two problems appeared responsible for this situation. First, breakdowns reduced the available working time during the season and the useful life to less than the 6 years assumed in the loan repayment schedule. Second, as the number of tractors introduced increased use declined.

The low man-to-land ratio suggests a shortage of labor (human and animal) for land preparation in Sidrap and Pinrang. And because minitractors did not displace hired labor (Bernsten 1981) there were no negative social welfare impacts. Yet, unless the life of the tractors can be extended to at least 5 full years, and their number held down to a level allowing for sufficient use of each, tractors will not be an economically feasible alternative to existing techniques.

REFERENCES CITED

Abbas, S. 1977. Perspective of agricultural mechanization in Indonesia and South Sulawesi. Ujung Pandang.

Agricultural Extension Service. 1980. Internal data on tractor sales in the province. Ujung Pandang, South Sulawesi.

Agricultural Extension Service and Association of Devotees of Agricultural Mechanization in Indonesia. 1976. Feasibility study of tractor development in Barru, Enrekang, and Tona Toraja Districts, South Sulawesi. Ujung Pandang.

Bernsten, R. H. 1981. Effect of minitractor mechanization on employment and labor use intensity, Sidrap and Pinrang Districts, South Sulawesi, Indonesia. The Consequences of Small Rice Farm Mechanization Project Working Paper 32. Los Baños, Laguna.

B. P. S. (Biro Pusat Statistik). 1980. Statistical handbook of Indonesia. Jakarta.

Consequences Team. 1981. Consequences of land preparation mechanization in Indonesia: South Sulawesi and West Java. Paper presented at the Regional Seminar on Appropriate Mechanization for Rural Development, Jakarta, Indonesia.

Directorate for Technical Agriculture. 1979. Survey for the possibility of using small tractors in Sidrap and Pinrang Districts, South Sulawesi. Jakarta.

Directorate of Food Crops. 1975. Tractor development study in Gowa, Maros, Pangkep, Polmas, and Soppeng Districts, South Sulawesi. Jakarta.

Gadjah Mada University. 1976. Survey for agricultural tractor development at Bantaeng, Bulukumba, Sinjai, Wajo, Bone-Bone, Tekalar, Luwu Districts, South Sulawesi. Faculty of Agriculture, Yogyakarta.

Parusengi, D. 1972. Possibility of using small tractor for people's farming in South Sulawesi. Fatometa IPB, Bogor, Indonesia.

Team on Selective Mechanization. 1979. Owning and operating a tractor in South Sulawesi (manual). Ujung Pandang.

ECONOMICS OF PUMP IRRIGATION IN EASTERN NEPAL

M. R. Khoju

Data were collected from 92 rainfed and 97 pump-irrigated farms
in the terai of the Eastern Development Region of Nepal. Results
suggest that pump irrigation has promoted cropping intensity,
higher levels of resource use, and higher crop yields. More than
79% of the increase in improved rice, local rice, and wheat yields
and 34% of the increase in cropping intensity were attributed to
irrigation. Pump irrigation also increased employment through
increase in labor input per crop and in cropping intensity. Net farm
income for a 4.54-ha, pump-irrigated farm was estimated at $544,
compared with $334 for a similar sized rainfed farm. The results
supported the current program for expansion of pump irrigation in
the terai of eastern Nepal.

In Nepal, agriculture contributes around two-thirds of gross domestic product,
provides 80% of total export earnings, and employs about 94% of the total labor
force. Low productivity, as well as underemployment of the agricultural labor force,
has contributed to an average per capita income of only $79 in this sector compared
to the national average of $120 (Upadhyay 1981). FAO has reported that nearly
two-thirds of the rural population live in absolute poverty. With few growth options
available, and in view of the very heavy dependence on agriculture, economic
development depends on the growth of agriculture. His Majesty's Government of
Nepal has, therefore, been allocating a considerable proportion of the total capital
outlay in each of six 5-year plans for the development of agriculture, including the
expansion of irrigation facilities.

The National Development Plan emphasizes the urgent need for shallow wells to
provide irrigation for effective growth in agriculture (Asian Development Bank
1980). Irrigation allows planting of more than one crop on the same land in a year,
providing greater use of resources. However, as of 1979-80, only 13.6% of the
cultivated area was irrigated. In addition to the government-owned projects, privately owned small projects, often using pumpsets, are helping to expand the

Agricultural Development Bank, Nepal.

irrigated area. Pump irrigation is becoming increasingly popular in most of the terai districts of Nepal. Most of the pumpsets are 5-hp capacity and lift water from ground (shallow tubewell, dugwell) and surface water sources, supplying an average area of 5 ha. While large irrigation projects require huge investment and a long development period, pump irrigation is an easy and cheap way to develop the farmers' irrigation systems rapidly. Since pump irrigation is controlled by individual farmers, they can get water whenever needed without outside constraints.

The government's objective in expanding pump irrigation is to promote the adoption of seed-fertilizer technology and increase cropping intensity, which will increase land productivity, employment opportunities, and the net income of farmers with pumpsets.

HISTORY OF PUMP IRRIGATION IN NEPAL

Pump irrigation has been practiced in Nepal since the early 1960s when early adopters purchased pumpsets from nearby Indian border towns. In 1964, the privately owned Kalpana Trading Company became the Nepalese distributor of Indian-made Kirloskar diesel engine pumpsets. In the succeeding years, farmers continued buying in the local and Indian border markets. Pump irrigation received a major boost in 1969 when the former Land Reform Saving Corporation (LRSC) imported 1,000 units from Japan. From its inception in 1967, the Agricultural Development Bank (the LRSC was merged with the bank in 1973) started financing the agricultural sector. In 1975, two other commercial banks, Rastriya Baniya Bank and Nepal Bank, following a directive from the Nepal Rastra Bank, began providing finance for agricultural enterprises including pumpsets. With increased farmer awareness of the usefulness of pump irrigation, pumpset demand rose rapidly. The Agricultural Development Bank imported 1,160 in 1976 and 1,400 in 1978 as part of the second and third Agricultural Credit Projects funded by the Asian Development Bank. The Agricultural Inputs Corporation import of 898 pumpsets in 1976 was in addition to regular imports by private dealers. With all of this activity, pumpset numbers increased to more than 9,200 in 1979. Assuming, on the average, a 5-ha command area/pumpset, some 46,000 ha about 3% of the total cultivated area in the terai are currently irrigated by pumpsets.

Most of the integrated agricultural projects now have provision for expansion of pump irrigation. Consequently 5,900 pumpsets were targeted for distribution in the sixth five-year plan period (1980-85).

OBJECTIVES

The objectives of the study were:
1. To determine the production, employment, and income effects of pump irrigation;
2. To document the land utilization pattern and adoption of high yielding varieties of crops on rainfed and pump-irrigated farms;
3. To study the impact of pump irrigation on input use, crop yields, and crop income per hectare; and
4. To assess the profitability of owning irrigation pumps.

STUDY AREA AND SAMPLE

The Jhapa, Morang, Sunsari, and Saptari terai districts in the Eastern Development Region of Nepal (Fig. 1) were selected because farmers there were early adopters of the new technology. In each district, the four village panchayat with the most pumpsets were identified (Fig. 2), and seven farmers with and seven without pumpsets were randomly selected from each. The primary cross-section data on socioeconomic characteristics, cropping pattern, pumpset type and use, inputs use, and crop production, etc. for November 1978 to October 1979 were collected through personal interviews of 224 farmers. Because of time constraints and lack of data from some respondents, a sample of 189 was used for the analysis. The distribution of the farmers by district is in Table 1.

RESULTS

Socioeconomic characteristics
The two farmer groups differed in some socioeconomic characteristics (Table 2). The pumpset owners had larger landholdings, larger household size, and were more educated than their slightly older counterparts without pumpsets.

Impact of pump irrigation on land use
Agricultural production can be increased through higher cropping intensity, increased crop yields, or both. To study the impact of pump irrigation on land use, cropping patterns and cropping intensities for rainfed and pump-irrigated farms were compared (Table 3). Rice and wheat were the predominant crops on both types of farm, although on the pump-irrigated farms a larger percentage of the cultivated area was allocated to high yielding, improved rice and wheat. Cropping intensity was higher on farms with pump irrigation because assured irrigation allowed farmers to cultivate a larger area of wheat in winter.

Table 1. Total sample farms, by district.

District	Farmers (no.)		
	Rainfed farm	Pump-irrigated farm	Total
Jhapa	23	23	46
Morang	21	27	48
Sunsari	24	23	47
Saptari	24	24	48
Total	92	97	189

Table 2. Socioeconomic characteristics of the sample farmers.

Characteristic	Rainfed farms	Pump-irrigated farms
Average size of landholding (ha)	3.6	4.5
Size of household (no.)	8.4	9.6
Farmers schooling (yr)	5.0	7.8
Age of the farmer (yr)	39.6	38.8

1. The study areas (a. Saptari, b. Sunsari, c. Morang, d. Jhapa) in Nepal.

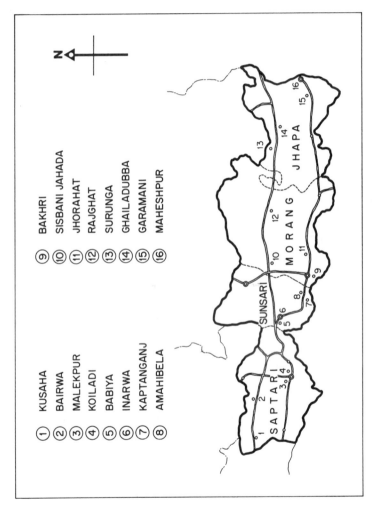

① KUSAHA		⑨ BAKHRI	
② BAIRWA		⑩ SISBANI JAHADA	
③ MALEKPUR		⑪ JHORAHAT	
④ KOILADI		⑫ RAJGHAT	
⑤ BABIYA		⑬ SURUNGA	
⑥ INARWA		⑭ GHAILADUBBA	
⑦ KAPTANGANJ		⑮ GARAMANI	
⑧ AMAHIBELA		⑯ MAHESHPUR	

2. Study areas showing sample village panchayat.

Table 3. Cropping pattern and cropping intensity on rainfed and pump-irrigated sample farms.

Crop	Rainfed farms		Pump-irrigated farms	
	Area (ha)	% of total cultivated (area)	Area (ha)	% of total cultivated area
Improved rice	0.13	3.52	1.09	23.99
Local rice	2.95	81.46	3.04	66.87
Wheat	0.41	11.52	1.63	35.97
Other crops[a]	0.78	21.50	1.14	25.17
Total	4.27		6.90	
Cropping intensity[b]	118.00%		152.00%	
Sample size	92		97	

[a]Includes jute, maize, mustard, pulses, and ragi.

[b]Cropping intensity = $\dfrac{\text{total cropped area in one agricultural year}}{\text{total cultivated area}} \times 100$.

Impact of pump irrigation on input use and crop yields

Input levels and yields per hectare of improved rice, local rice and wheat for rainfed and pump-irrigated farms were compared (Table 4). Pump irrigation eliminates reliance on monsoon rains, and promotes the use of higher levels of inputs. As a result, the yields of all three crops were higher on pump-irrigated farms.

The use of manure and fertilizer, plant protection, and human labor were all higher on the pump-irrigated farms. Human labor, measured in man-days of 8 working hours, comprised all labor used for operations other than harvesting and threshing. The impact of pump irrigation on total labor use would have been even greater if labor required for these operations had been included. The higher cropping intensity on pump-irrigated farms also resulted in even larger differences in human labor and plow use per hectare. The most plausible reason for the differences in inputs and output is that, on rainfed farms, agricultural production depends on the monsoon, so farmers try to reduce risk by using lower levels of inputs.

Impact of pump irrigation on costs and revenue

Total revenue, total costs, and net revenue per hectare of improved rice, local rice, and wheat are in Table 5. Pump-irrigated farms had a 51% higher net revenue for improved rice, 47% higher for local rice, and 125% higher for wheat. The higher net revenue resulted from irrigation and more inputs per hectare. The additional cost of these inputs was less than the additional revenue generated.

Covariance analysis

The higher levels of inputs, including the employment of human labor and the higher cropping intensity on pump-irrigated farms, were not necessarily associated with pump irrigation. The differences between the pump-irrigated and rainfed farms might be associated with variables not controlled in the survey, such as size of landholding, years of schooling of the farmer and his father, tractor use in land preparation, asset position, and location and interaction effects between pump

Table 4. Input use and crop yields on rainfed and pump-irrigated crops.[a]

Item	Improved rice		Local rice		Wheat	
	Rainfed	Pump-irrigated	Rainfed[b]	Pump-irrigated	Rainfed	Pump-irrigated[c]
Sample size (no.)	25	37	119	56	32	98
Manure and fertilizer ($/ha)	10.33	23.42	4.17	7.67	25.42	45.83
	(12.42)	(25.00)	(9.50)	(10.92)	(20.67)	(22.50)
Plant protection ($/ha)	2.58	3.00	0.08	0.42	0.25	1.42
	(3.00)	(5.00)	(0.50)	(0.92)	(1.00)	(3.08)
Plow unit (days/ha)[d]	34	38	31	30	35	35
	(6)	(9)	(6)	(8)	(10)	(15)
Human labor (days/ha)[e]	39	64	48	55	21	25
	(14)	(24)	(27)	(16)	(14)	(18)
Crop yield (kg/ha)	1803	2636	1352	1813	1169	2051
	(385)	(393)	(287)	(386)	(247)	(555)

[a]Figures in parentheses are standard deviations. [b]Includes rainfed local rice cultivated by farmers with pump irrigation. [c]Includes wheat cultivated on rainfed farm by renting pump irrigation. [d]Measured in days of 8 working hours and comprises one man and a pair of bullocks. [e]Measured in man-days of 8 working hours.

Table 5. Revenues and costs of rainfed and pump-irrigated crops.[a]

Item	Improved rice		Local rice		Wheat	
	Rainfed	Pump-irrigated	Rainfed	Pump-irrigated	Rainfed	Pump-irrigated
Sample size (no.)	25	37	119	56	32	98
Total revenue ($/ha)	243	353	179	234	185	328
	(55)	(60)	(38)	(48)	(38)	(105)
Total costs[b] ($/ha)	127	177	117	143	128	200
	(23)	(50)	(25)	(27)	(26)	(38)
Net revenue ($/ha)	116	175	62	91	57	128
	(56)	(68)	(39)	(50)	(39)	(97)

[a]Figures in parentheses are standard deviations. [b]Excluding fixed costs of pump irrigation.

irrigation and mechanization. A covariance analysis was used to isolate the effects of these other variables, and thus to determine the impact of pump irrigation.

A covariance model was estimated for dependent variables where observed differences between rainfed and pump-irrigated farms were statistically significant: cropping intensity, use of human labor, manures and fertilizers, crop yield, and net revenue per hectare. The relationship used was:

$$Y_i = a_0 + \sum_{j=1}^{10} a_j x_j + e$$

for $i = 1, \ldots, 5$

where:

Y_1 is cropping intensity;

Y_2 is human labor (days/ha);

Y_3 is manures and fertilizers ($/ha);

Y_4 is crop yield (kg/ha);

Y_5 is net revenue ($/ha);

x_1 is the pump irrigation dummy, taking a value of one if the crop is pump-irrigated and zero otherwise;

x_2 is size of landholding (ha);

x_3 is education of the farmer (yr);

x_4 is education of the farmer's father (yr);

x_5 is a mechanization dummy taking a value of one if a tractor is used in land preparation and zero otherwise;

x_6 is the value of the farmer's assets ($);

x_7 is a district dummy taking a value of one if the observation is from Jhapa district and zero otherwise;

x_8 is a district dummy taking a value of one if the observation is from Morang district and zero otherwise;

x_9 is a district dummy taking a value of one if the observation is from Sunsari district and zero otherwise;

x_{10} is the interaction term between pump irrigation (x_1) and mechanization (x_5);

a_0 is the intercept (constant) term;

a_1 to a_{10} are regression coefficients of the respective independent variables; and

e is the random error.

Human labor (days/ha), plow units (days/ha), manures and fertilizers ($/ha), and plant protection ($/ha) were included as additional explanatory variables in the crop yield model.

The mechanization dummy (x_5) and interaction term between mechanization and pump irrigation (x_{10}) were excluded from the cropping intensity model because of limited observations. The pump irrigation dummy (x_1) was assigned on the basis of whether the farm was pump irrigated (1) or rainfed (0).

The results of the five covariance analyses are summarized in Table 6. The coefficients for pump irrigation are all positive and significant, indicating that pump irrigation is associated with increased cropping intensity, input use, crop yields, and

Table 6. Results of covariance analysis.

Dependent variable	Differences between means	Coefficient of pump irrigation dummy[a]	Other important variables[b]
Cropping intensity (%)	34.0	34.6*	Size of holding (+)
Human labor[c] (days/ha)			
Improved rice	24.5	16.2*	Size of holding (+) District dummy
Wheat	14.0	14.1*	None
Manure and fertilizer ($/ha)			
Improved rice	13.1	13.8*	None
Local rice	3.5	1.2	Mechanical land preparation (+)
Wheat	20.4	17.5*	Mechanical land preparation (+)
Crop yield (kg/ha)			
Improved rice	833	685.8*	Size of holding (+) District dummy
Local rice	461	367.2*	Size of holding (+) Mechanical land preparation (+)
Wheat	992	721.7*	District dummy District dummy
Net revenue ($/ha)			
Improved rice	59.3	34.3**	District dummy Size of holding (−)
Local rice	29.0	23.7	Mechanical land preparation (+)
Wheat	71.2	65.6	Mechanical land preparation (+)
		16.2	District dummy

[a]*Significant at 1% level. **Significant at 5% level. [b]Symbols in parentheses are observed signs. [c]For local rice preharvest labor for rainfed and pump-irrigated conditions did not significantly differ.

net revenue for all crops. More detailed results are reported in Khoju (1980). It appears that, on the average, irrigation is the major factor associated with increased cropping intensity, input use, and yield.

Profitability of pump use
Pump irrigation seems to be contributing to increased production through facilitating adoption of improved rice and wheat varieties and to an increase in cropping intensity. However, with increasing prices of diesel and other inputs, the costs of cultivation are increasing. At this stage, the question of whether farmers are making, and will continue to make, profits by owning pumpsets is important. To answer this question, net farm incomes were computed for rainfed and pump-irrigated farms based on the following assumptions:

1. The size of the pump-irrigated farm was 4.54 ha; the same size was assumed for the rainfed farm.
2. The average cropping patterns and cropping intensities of rainfed and pump-irrigated farms were used.

3. Cultivation costs and revenues per hectare of rainfed and pump-irrigated improved rice, local rice, and wheat were based on Table 5; costs and revenues of other crops were computed from the survey data reported in Khoju (1980).
4. Average annual renting out of the pumpset was 59 hours. The rental rate was $0.89/hour, whereas the variable cost per hour of pump set operation was $0.35.
5. The average costs of pumpset and tubewell were $583 and $167, respectively. These were purchased at 14% interest/annum payable in equal installments over 5 years.
6. Repair and maintenance costs of pumpset and tubewell were estimated at $21/year.

The benefits and costs for rainfed and pump-irrigated farms, based on the above assumptions, are in Tables 7 and 8. They reveal higher total costs and total revenue on pump-irrigated farms. The net farm income from pump-irrigated farms was also higher — $544, 63% higher than the $334 of rainfed farms with the same landholding.

CONCLUSIONS

Results of the covariance analysis showed that most of the observed differences in cropping intensity, input use, crop yields, and net revenue between the rainfed and pump-irrigated farms could be attributed to pump irrigation. Farmers with pump irrigation were able to produce more per unit of time from the same land area, thereby obtaining higher net farm incomes. Pump irrigation increased employment by increasing use of human labor per unit of cultivated land and by employing labor for winter crops made possible by assured irrigation.

The results justify the present program of expanding pump irrigation. However, even better results may be expected if two shortcomings in the present pumpset

Table 7. Computed net income[a] and cropping intensity[b] in a 4.54-ha rainfed farm.

Crop	Area (ha)	Cost of cultivation ($/ha)	Total cost of cultivation ($)	Revenue ($/ha)	Total revenue ($)
Improved rice	0.16	127	20	243	39
Local rice	3.70	117	434	179	663
Wheat	0.52	128	66	185	96
Jute	0.38	236	90	301	114
Maize	0.20	87	17	132	26
Mustard	0.17	73	12	143	24
Pulses	0.19	18	3	66	13
Ragi	0.04	64	3	86	3
Total	5.36		646		980

[a]Net income = total revenue – total costs
$$= 980 - 646$$
$$= \$334$$
[b]Cropping intensity = $\dfrac{5.36}{4.54} \times 100 = 118\%$.

Table 8. Computed net income[a] and cropping intensity[b] in a 4.54-ha pump-irrigated farm.

Crop	Area (ha)	Cost of cultivation ($/ha)	Total cost of cultivation ($)	Revenue ($/ha)	Total revenue ($)
Improved rice	1.09	177	193	353	385
Local rice	3.04	143	435	234	712
Wheat	1.63	200	326	328	535
Jute	0.52	236	123	301	157
Maize	0.15	98	15	162	24
Mustard	0.20	73	15	143	29
Pulses	0.22	18	4	66	15
Ragi	0.05	64	3	86	4
Total	6.90		1114		1860
Pump irrigation:					
Fixed cost	–	–	234	–	–
Variable cost	–	–	21[c]	–	53[d]
Grand toral	–	–	1369	–	1913

[a]Net income = 1913 – 1369 = 544.

[b]Cropping intensity = $\frac{6.90}{4.54}$ × 100 = 152%. [c]Includes variable cost of 59 hours rented out at $0.35/h. [d]Includes revenue from 50 hours rented out at $0.89/h.

distribution program are overcome. First, the funding agency requirement of at least 3 ha as the project area before approving loans, discourages most farmers from applying. Second, all farmers with 3 ha or more are given the same size of pumpset (generally 5 hp) regardless of actual crop water requirements. Policies to overcome these problems and to assist in providing irrigation facilities for smaller farmers (possibly through selling lower capacity pumps) should have high priority.

REFERENCES CITED

Asian Development Bank. 1980. Final report of the Fourth Agricultural Credit Project, Nepal. Agricultural Finance Corporation, Bombay, India.

Khoju, M. R. 1980. The economics of pump-irrigation in eastern Nepal. MS thesis, University of the Philippines at Los Baños, Laguna.

Upadhyay, S. K. 1981. Case studies in innovative credit scheme. Paper presented at the International Seminar on Harnessing the Financial System in Support of Rural Development, Poona, India. 2-6 June.

EFFECT OF TUBEWELLS ON INCOME AND EMPLOYMENT: A CASE STUDY IN THREE VILLAGES IN KEDIRI, EAST JAVA, INDONESIA

T. Sudaryanto

Indonesia is developing groundwater sources for agricultural purposes by using tubewells. Data were collected from 66 tubewell users, 53 nonusers, and 30 farm laborers to investigate the effects on farm income and employment, and the feasibility of tubewell investment. Users were categorized by the number of years they had been using tubewell irrigation. Farm analyses for two alternative cropping systems indicated tubewell introduction, increased cropping intensity, production, and farm income. The increase in income varied with experience in tubewell operation. Financially, *rice - rice - soybean* was better than *rice - rice - maize*, yet economically the reverse was true. Tubewells were financially and economically feasible. Tubewells also generated increased employment and income for laborers. Sensitivity analysis showed that the program would still be profitable to farmers even if they paid the whole cost of the project.

Increasing food production remains the first priority of agricultural development in Indonesia. The program efforts aim to increase production and crop area. The latter is done primarily outside Java through the opening of new tidal swamp and upland areas. However, the rate of increase in output is not very promising. Within the first two 5-year development plans (Pelita I and II), annual rice production increased 4.6% and 3.8%, respectively. Still, the demand for rice was increasing at 4-5% per annum (Teken 1974, Mears 1976) because of population growth, income growth, and a shift in diet to rice.

The constraints in rice production through the intensification program can be divided into those preventing an increase in the area suitable for intensification and those preventing yield improvement at the given intensity level (Teken and Kuncoro 1978). Between 1974 and 1976, the area suitable for intensification increased at only 4.5% per annum. The limitation was more apparent in the dry season when, only 47% of the 5.5 million ha of lowland in Indonesia can be devoted to rice (Montgo-

Center for Agro-Economic Research, Bogor, Indonesia.

mery 1979). For Java, the figure is only 35% of 3.0 million ha. Irrigation is the limiting factor.

The government continues to develop irrigation infrastructure to support rice intensification. Within Pelita I, 1.6 million ha of irrigation facilities have been improved, or extended. Irrigation for about 765,000 ha will be developed in Pelita III. This area is serviced by dams, water tanks, and rivers. In addition, the development of groundwater resources has been initiated through pilot projects of the Project for Groundwater Development (P2AT), Directorate General for Irrigation, Ministry of Public Works. Pilot projects are in Gunung Kidul (DIY), Madiun (East Java), Semani (West Sumatra), Kediri and Nganjuk (East Java), and Madura (East Java).

With tubewell introduction, crop area is expected to increase, particularly in the dry season, and the production increases should cover additional costs. Yet little is known about the magnitudes of such costs and returns. Besides farm income, employment opportunities are of special concern in Pelita III. The effect of the program should be traced to the impact on employment opportunities and income distribution. These impacts of tubewell introduction are investigated in this study.

Brief outline of the P2AT project in Kediri and Nganjuk
In Kediri and Nganjuk, 37,000 ha are considered to have good potential for groundwater development and about 1,100 tubewells would be needed for the whole area (P2AT 1979). Sixty-nine tubewells, servicing 2,945 ha, were operating at the end of 1979.

Centrifugal, turbine, and submersible pumps were all found in the project area. In Plemahan, however, all were turbines powered by Lister and Bedford diesel engines from 22.7 to 65.0 hp, which discharged water from 24 to 60 liters per second. Data on the depth of each tubewell were not available, but the average was about 47 m. The area irrigated by each tubewell ranged from 23.6 to 51.8 ha with an average of 42.0 ha. To facilitate water distribution, the area was divided into 4-7 irrigation blocks each from 2.8 to 15.0 ha, depending on topography and distance from the pump. Each pump was managed directly by the village headman assisted in daily operations by an operations manager, secretary, treasurer, water manager, and pump operator. Water distribution was based on a rotation system with intervals of 7 days for rice and 14 days for upland crops. To obtain an allotment, a farmer had to apply to the block leader 1 day ahead of schedule. The application would be sent to the Jogotirto, a village official in charge of irrigation, and finally to the tubewell operator.

Objectives
The objectives of the study were:
1. To determine the effect of tubewells on cropping pattern, cropping intensity, level of input use, production, farm and laborer incomes , and employment;
2. To estimate the benefit cost ratio (B:C), internal rate of return (IRR), and net present value (NPV) of investment in tubewells in both financial and economic terms.

METHODOLOGY

Theoretical framework

Farm production is dependent on a combination of environmental and management factors (Zandstra 1979). Environmental factors are the physical ones of land, water, solar energy, temperature and moisture, and the nonphysical ones of labor and capital. Farm production can be increased by improving environmental quality or by improving management.

Improved irrigation facilities result in changed water availability and in increased crop production and cropping intensity. Furthermore, irrigation improvements will also facilitate adoption of fertilizer, high yielding varieties (HYV), and pesticides (Munandar 1978). So, improvements to an irrigation system will have both direct and indirect effects on production.

The effect of tubewells can be determined either by comparing user and nonuser farms or comparing individual farms before and after tubewells. In the first approach environmental factors are assumed to be the same across farms. In the second approach technological changes, other than tubewells, are assumed to be absent over time. Since it was considered unlikely that Javanese farmers would be able to recall accurately changes in costs and earnings over time, they were estimated as the differences between users and nonusers. Comparisons of cropping patterns, cropped areas, types and levels of inputs used, and output were made using data relating to before and after the introduction of tubewells because recall of these was believed to be sufficiently reliable. Data on farm laborer employment and incomes before and after tubewell introduction were collected in interviews with laborers in the areas with tubewells. No laborers from the areas without tubewells were interviewed because most migrated elsewhere to find work.

Sampling

The Project for Ground Water Development in Kediri-Nganjuk area had three centers — Plemahan with 32 tubewells in 8 villages; Keras with 22 tubewells in 18 villages, and Nganjuk with 11 tubewells in 6 villages.

Most tubewells in Plemahan were in the villages of Sidowarek (13 units), Sukoharjo (3 units), and Plemahan (6 units). Each of the other villages had only one or

Table 1. Category breakdown of farmer and laborer respondents.

Category	Respondents (no.)			
	Sidowarek	Ringinpitu	Sukoharjo	Total
Tubewell users by years of experience				
1 yr	17	–	–	17
2 yr	14	–	–	14
3 yr	–	–	15	15
5 yr	20	–	–	20
Total	51	–	15	66
Nonusers	–	38	15	53
Farm laborers	20	–	10	30

two tubewells. Since a compact and homogeneous survey area was required, Sido-warek and Sukoharjo were selected. The tubewells were classified by years of operation. Sample farmers were randomly selected for each of the tubewells to capture differences in tubewell performance resulting from differences in power rating and adequacy of groundwater resources. The sample farmers were then aggregated into each stratum (Table 1).

Nonusers were selected from Sukoharjo and Ringinpitu, the latter being close to Sidowarek. Samples of 10 and 20 laborer households were randomly drawn from Sukoharjo and Sidowarek, respectively. Laborer households were defined as those whose major source of income was wage labor.

Data collection and analysis

A preliminary survey determined the village samples, sampling frame, and cropping pattern. Village officials and tubewell operators were interviewed. Secondary data on investments were collected from the P2AT project file and other variables from the district agricultural office, agricultural extension center (BPP), and village offices. The main survey data were collected through individual interviews.

Farm income and labor absorption were analyzed manually. Feasibility analysis of tubewells was based on economic and financial estimates of the B:C, IRR, and NPV.

The observations for each crop in the farm analysis are in Table 2. There was no analysis for maize in the 3-year category there being only one observation.

Sensitivity analysis

In the financial and economic analyses, the magnitude of B:C, IRR, and NVP is influenced by changes in costs and the interest rate. So, it is necessary to conduct sensitivity analyses to determine how critical the results are to changes in factor prices. The following sensitivity analyses were completed:

1. 10% decrease in revenue;
2. 10% increase in cost;
3. 25% decrease in revenue;
4. 25% increase in cost;
5. investment cost paid by farmers; and
6. investment cost paid by farmers with revenue decreasing by 25%.

Analyses 1 and 2 were used for economic analysis only. The rest were used for economic and financial analyses.

RESULTS AND DISCUSSION

Changes in farm management

Cropping patterns. With an annual average rainfall of 216 mm in 83 days, cropping patterns in Plemahan were dependent on the availability of supplementary water. Sixty percent of rainfed farms could only grow 1 or 2 crops annually, but 95% of the respondents using tubewells grew 3 or more. The most important crops were rice, soybean, and maize. The various cropping patterns are in Table 3.

Rice dominated all cropping patterns because it is the most profitable, and

Table 2. Number of observations for each crop.

Category	Observations (no.)			
	Wet season rice	Dry season rice	Soybean	Maize
Tubewell users by years of experience				
1 yr	17	14	6	11
2 yr	13	9	10	8
3 yr	15	13	14	1
5 yr	25	15	15	9
Nonusers	48	–	43	21

Table 3. Distribution of cropping patterns on sample farms.

Cropping pattern	Distribution (%)				
	Tubewell users				Nonusers
	1 yr	2 yr	3 yr	5 yr	
Rice – rice – soybean	35	36	73	45	0
Rice – rice – maize	23	36	7	20	0
Rice – soybean – maize	0	7	0	5	23
Others					
1 crop/yr	0	0	0	0	3
2 crops/yr	12	0	6	0	57
3 crops/yr	18	21	7	10	0
4 crops/yr	12	0	7	20	17

subsistence farmers tend to consume what they grow. The majority of nonusers, who could only grow two crops a year, grew a single rice crop followed by an upland crop.

The patterns selected for income analysis were rice - rice - soybean for tubewell users, compared to rice - soybean for nonusers, and rice - rice - maize for users compared to rice - soybean - maize for nonusers.

Cropping intensity. Cropping intensity is important to the land's annual income potential. Tubewell users, who could triple-crop, achieved a cropping intensity of 300%, whereas nonusers realized only 256% for the rice - soybean - maize pattern and 196% for rice - soybean.

Seed, fertilizer, and pesticide use. Comparisons were only possible for the wet season rice crop because soybean and maize were grown by tubewell users in the wet season (September-November) and nonusers in the dry season (May-July). Dry season rice was grown only by tubewell users.

In the wet season, IR36 was grown by all tubewell users and 80% of the nonusers. Before tubewell introduction, 68% of the respondents grew PB5 and PB8, the rest grew IR36, Pelita, and local varieties. IR36 adoption was in response to the serious brown planthopper infestation in 1976-77.

Seed and fertilizer use by both groups is shown in Table 4. Fertilizer use has undoubtedly increased; tubewell users tended to use marginally more than nonusers. No discernible pattern in seed use appeared. Pesticide use has similarly increased with little evidence of differences in level of use between the two groups.

Table 4. Comparison of seed and fertilizer use by tubewell users and nonusers for wet season rice.

Category	Seeds (kg/ha)		Fertilizer (kg/ha)	
	Before	After 1979-80	Before	After 1979-80
Tubewell users				
1 yr	33	34	391	483
2 yr	35	38	343	465
3 yr	55	54	285	480
5 yr	55	52	427	484
Nonusers	–	55	–	454

Table 5. Income analysis for rice, soybean, and maize.

Category (yr)	Yield (t/ha)	Value ($/ha)	Total cost ($/ha)	Net return ($/ha)
		Wet season rice		
User – 1	4.20	521	284	237
– 2	4.60	571	291	280
– 3	4.72	586	320	266
– 5	4.77	592	321	271
Nonuser	3.84	477	267	210
		Dry season rice		
User – 1	3.59	446	309	137
– 2	4.45	552	324	228
– 3	3.57	443	330	113
– 5	4.16	516	326	190
Nonuser[a]	–	–	–	–
		Soybean		
User – 1	0.58	246	251	–5
– 2	0.69	288	229	59
– 3	0.62	262	252	10
– 5	0.67	280	255	25
Nonuser	0.57	241	243	–2
		Maize		
User – 1	1.89	241	273	–32
– 2	2.44	310	294	16
– 3[a]	–	–	–	–
– 5	1.98	252	297	–45
Nonuser	1.64	206	249	–43

[a]No crop in this category.

Farm income analysis

Farm incomes, based on the cropping patterns and cropping intensities, were calculated as total net return. Yields, costs, and returns per hectare for each crop are in Table 5. To estimate total costs, family labor was charged at the prevailing wage rate and seed at the purchase price.

Table 6. Difference in net farm incomes for users and nonusers of pump irrigation.[a]

Cropping pattern	Category (yr)		Net farm income ($/ha)	Increase over rice – soybean ($/ha)	Increase over rice – soybean – maize ($/ha)
Rice – rice – soybean	User	– 1	369	161 (77)	192 (108)
		– 2	567	359 (172)	390 (220)
		– 3	389	181 (87)	212 (119)
		– 5	486	278 (133)	309 (174)
Rice – rice – maize	User	– 1	342	134 (64)	165 (93)
		– 2	524	316 (152)	347 (196)
		– 5	416	208 (100)	239 (135)
Rice – soybean	Nonuser		208	–	–
Rice – soybean – maize	Nonuser		177	–	–

[a]Values in parentheses are percentages.

The annual increases in net farm income from the irrigated crop patterns compared to the rainfed patterns are in Table 6. Increases ranged from 64% during the first year of tubewell use for rice - rice - maize compared to rainfed rice - soybean, to 220% during the second year of tubewell use for rice - rice - soybean compared to rainfed rice - soybean - maize. The increase in income from tubewell use is due to increases in cropping intensity and production for each of the crops.

Financial and economic analyses

Costs and benefits. The total cost consists of investment costs, operation and maintenance costs, and farm costs. Benefits were measured as the value of the increase in farm output. Investment costs can be divided into capital and support facility costs. Capital costs cover well, canal, and road construction; power source; and miscellaneous items such as fuel containers. The market and shadow costs of the capital investment and support facilities are in Table 7. Operation and maintenance costs, which cover fuel, oil, grease, pump, and machine repairs and operator salary, had market price values of $888 to $1,350/unit ($20.5-39.4/ha). The economic value ranged from $1,693 to $2,301/unit ($38.2-66.2/ha).

Returns from the project were calculated as the difference between gross returns with and without the tubewells. The two irrigated cropping patterns discussed earlier were compared to the single rainfed pattern of rice - soybean.

Based on the lifetime of a tubewell with proper repair and maintenance, the project life was assumed to be 51 years. Building construction and purchase of project facilities were assumed done the first year. Drilling was assumed to begin the second year, together with the purchase of pump and accessories, installment, and canal construction. Operations would then begin the third year.

The annual flow of benefits was assumed to increase from the third to the eighth year and then remain constant. Benefits were estimated at constant prices, based on the price level in the study period (Table 8).

Results of investment analysis. The results of the investment analysis are in Table 9. In the financial analysis of the base model, using a discount rate of 12% the B:C for both irrigated patterns was in excess of 2.0 and the IRR was >50%. The rice - rice - soybean pattern was superior to rice - rice - maize. From an economic

Table 7. Capital and support facility costs of tubewell investment.[a]

Cost component	Market cost ($)	Shadow cost ($)
Well construction	4,891	4,860
Tubewell building and facilities	3,139	2,731
Canal construction	1,122	801
Pump and accessories	18,967	18,967
Others	24	24
Total tubewell cost	28,143	27,383
Supporting project facilities	3,826	3,737
Total investment cost	31,969	31,120

[a]Source: Hunting Technical Services Ltd. and Sir. M. McDonald & Partners (1980).

Table 8. Annual gross benefits from tubewell investment.

Year	Rice – rice – soybean		Rice – rice – maize	
	Market price	Shadow price	Market price	Shadow price
1	–	–	–	–
2	–	–	–	–
3	505	623	500	755
4	547	716	534	799
5	584	710	570	841
6	634	771	610	895
7	680	826	652	947
8-51	732	884	696	1,001

Table 9. Base and sensitivity analyses of tubewell investment.[a]

Cropping pattern	Assumption	Financial analysis			Economic analysis		
		B:C	IRR (%)	NPV ($)	B:C	IRR (%)	NPV ($)
Rice – rice – soybean	Base	2.43	50	2589	1.19	29.8	836
	b	ne	ne	ne	1.07	18.5	302
	c	ne	ne	ne	1.08	20.1	380
	d	1.82	50	1489	0.89	1	–501
	e	2.06	50	2136	0.95	4.9	–292
	f	1.76	50	3021	ne	ne	ne
	g	1.32	30.3	800	ne	ne	ne
Rice – rice – maize	Base	2.33	50	2414	1.47	49.6	1978
	b	ne	ne	ne	1.33	36.2	1363
	c	ne	ne	ne	1.34	37.4	1560
	d	1.75	50	1358	1.11	20.2	440
	e	2.01	50	2122	1.18	27.8	934
	f	1.68	46.7	1717	ne	ne	ne
	g	1.26	26.5	665	ne	ne	ne

[a]ne = not estimated, B:C = benefit-cost ratio, IRR = internal rate of return, NPV = net present value. [b]10% decrease in revenue. [c]10% increase in costs. [d]25% decrease in revenue. [e]25% increase in costs. [f]Farmers pay investment costs. [g]Farmers pay investment costs plus 25% decrease in revenue.

viewpoint, neither pattern was highly profitable, largely because of the higher shadow prices of fertilizer and pesticides, but rice - rice - maize was superior to rice - rice - soybean. This reversal can be explained by the higher shadow price than market price of maize. All these patterns had a positive NPV.

Financially, the project was still profitable under either cropping pattern, with either a 25% increase in costs or 25% decrease in revenue. Economically, rice - rice - soybeans was unprofitable with or without tubewells. Similarly, if farmers had to pay the investment cost of the project, it would still be financially viable, even with a 25% drop in revenue.

Changes in employment opportunity

Tubewells, through their impact on cropping intensity and yield, are one form of mechanization which is likely to increase labor demand.

Labor absorption in farming. Family, hired, and total labor use per hectare for each crop is shown in Table 10. Aggregation in accordance with the observed cropping patterns generates labor use per hectare per annum (Table 11). For rice - rice - soybean compared to rice - soybean, labor use increased from 65% to 78%; for rice - rice - maize increase was between 70% and 77%.

Labor use and income. Information from farm laborers was used to examine three aspects of labor absorption before and after mechanization — variation of labor activity throughout the year, total labor used, and labor income. The impact of tubewells on each aspect is in Table 12. With the introduction of tubewells, farm laborers could find some work the whole year, and the amount of work in the busy

Table 10. Family, hired, and total labor use per hectare under irrigated and rainfed conditions.

Crop	Type of labor	Labor use (h) by tubewell user category				
		1 yr	2 yr	3 yr	5 yr	Nonuser
Wet season rice	Family	270	199	242	255	220
	Hired	955	1,083	1,153	1,133	952
	Total	1,225	1,282	1,395	1,388	1,172
Dry season rice	Family	322	219	215	250	–
	Hired	1,050	1,134	1,020	1,102	–
	Total	1,372	1,353	1,235	1,352	–
Soybean	Family	352	116	305	265	277
	Hired	721	656	581	522	657
	Total	1,073	772	886	787	934
Maize	Family	300	283	–	280	292
	Hired	612	637	–	647	493
	Total	912	920	–	927	785

Table 11. Differences in labor use by farmers using tubewells and by nonusers.[a]

Cropping pattern	Category (yr)	Labor use (h/ha)	Increase over rice – soybean (h/ha)	Increase over rice – soybean – maize (h/ha)
Rice – rice – soybean	User 1	3670	1600 (77)	1146 (43)
	2	3408	1338 (65)	884 (35)
	3	3690	1620 (78)	1166 (46)
	5	3528	1458 (70)	1004 (40)
Rice – rice – maize	User 1	3511	1441 (70)	987 (39)
	2	3555	1485 (72)	1031 (41)
	5	3668	1498 (77)	1144 (45)
Rice – soybean	Nonuser	2070	–	–
Rice – soybean – maize	Nonuser	2524	–	–

[a]Values in parentheses are percentages.

Table 12. Monthly variation in labor use and income of farm laborers before and after introduction of tubewells.

Variable	Before tubewell	After tubewell	Increase
Busy months (no.)	5	7	2
Slack months (no.)	4	5	1
Empty months (no.)	3	0	-3
Work h/ha per yr	838	1619	781
Income ($/ha per yr)	112	216	104

months increased. This resulted from the increase in cropping intensity and adoption of improved farm practices. All laborers said that it was easier to find jobs after the introduction of tubewells, and annual income increased by 93%. Labor migration between villages within the district also decreased. Before tubewells, 33% of the respondents migrated; after tubewells, migration dropped to 13%. The number of respondents moving beyond district borders appeared to be the same before and after. The lower rate of migration is consistent with the observation of increased work opportunities in the villages.

CONCLUSIONS AND RECOMMENDATIONS

Conclusions
Tubewell introduction has resulted in increased cropping intensity, yields, and income.

Estimated B:C, IRR, and NPV indicated that tubewell investment is feasible, both economically and financially. Financially the rice - rice - soybean pattern is much better than the rice - rice - maize pattern. Yet due to the relatively high shadow price of maize, the reverse is true in economic terms.

Sensitivity analysis showed tubewell investment remained feasible even with the whole investment and operation cost paid by farmers. This was true even with revenue reduced by 25%.

Tubewell introduction also resulted in increased employment opportunities and income for farm laborers. The highest labor use was found in the rice - rice - soybean pattern.

Recommendations
The success of tubewell investment in Plemahan supports extension to neighboring areas with high potential groundwater resources. Other areas should be explored to determine their potential for tubewell use.

The rice - rice - soybean pattern currently appears to be best for increasing farm income and employment opportunities. Yet, maize and soybean yields are far below those obtained in experiments because of the use of local varieties and low fertilizer levels. An intensification program for these crops is very much needed.

REFERENCES CITED

Hunting Technical Services Ltd. and Sir. M. McDonald and Partners. 1980. Kediri-Nganjuk Project Phase 3A, interim report. Directorate General of Water Resources Development, Jakarta.

Mears, L. 1976. Indonesia's food problems Pelita II/III. Ekonomi dan Keuangan Indonesia, 24(2).

Munandar, S. 1978. Pendapatan dan Distribusi Pendapatan Usahatani Padi di Berbagai Keadaan Irigasi. Tesis MS di Sekolah Pasca Sarjana, Institut Pertanian Bogor. Tidak Dipublikasikan.

Montgomery, R. 1979. Masalah Kekurangan Pangan, Momok Revolusi Hijau dan Sihir Kebijaksanaan Pangan. Agro Ekonomika 10(10).

P2AT. (Projek Pengembangan Air Tanah) 1979. Uraian Teknis Sub P2AT Kediri - Nganjuk. Direktorat Jenderal Pengairan, Jakarta.

Teken, I. B. 1974. Masalah Penyediaan Bahan Pangan di Indonesia. Prisma 3(6).

Teken, I. B., and Kuncoro. 1978. Kebijaksanaan Pengadaan Pangan Dewasa ini dan di Masa Datang. Mimbar Sosial Ekonomi, Departemen Ilmu-ilmu Sosial Ekonomi Pertanian, Fakultas Pertanian IPB, 1(1).

Zandstra, H. G. 1979. Cropping systems research for the Asian rice farmer. Agricultural Systems. Vol. 4.

COMPARATIVE ANALYSIS OF THRESHER ADOPTION AND USE IN THAILAND AND THE PHILIPPINES

F. Juarez and R. Pathnopas

This paper compares thresher adoption and use in Thailand and the Philippines. The history of thresher adoption and diffusion is traced, factors affecting adoption are reviewed, and the private costs and benefits measured. Factors such as irrigation, high yielding rice varieties, farm size, and credit facilities are shown to be correlated with adoption. Past and future investments were analyzed and benefits were found to be generally positive for owners and renters. The magnitude of benefits is believed to be the major reason for the recent rapid adoption of threshers.

In Thailand and the Philippines, mechanical rice threshers have recently replaced the traditional methods of animal, foot, and tractor treading and hand beating. Thus, they have become an important component in the rice production systems of both countries and have contributed to the shift from subsistence to commercial production. Portable and large axial-flow threshers were introduced in the Philippines in 1974-75 and in Thailand in 1975. With about 8,700 and 4,300 units produced and sold to date in the Philippines and Thailand, these two countries are the biggest users of the IRRI thresher in Asia (Fig. 1).

Although mechanization has been accepted as a possible major factor in improving farming efficiency, many constraints hinder the adoption of machines for harvesting and threshing. Khan (1971) pointed out that some farmers were reluctant to accept modern methods because of poor mechanical aptitude or inability to get financing. Rasanond et al (1977) found that acceptance of the IRRI axial-flow thresher was due largely to lower cost. In addition, in areas where double-cropping was widely practiced, the shorter time available for threshing and the scarcity of labor were major factors encouraging the adoption of modern threshing methods. Sison et al (1977) attempted to measure the costs, benefits, and return to various thresher investment in different areas of the Philippines.

The International Rice Research Institute and Mahidal University, Bangkok.

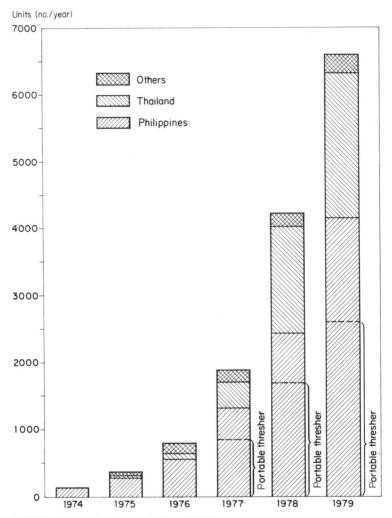

1. IRRI axial-flow thresher production, 1974-79.

The objective of this study was to compare the adoption of mechanical threshers in Thailand and the Philippines. In particular, we traced the history of thresher adoption and diffusion, examined the factors affecting adoption and use, and determined the private benefits and costs of ownership and use. The study concentrated on private costs and benefits although it is recognized that the social dimension should be added before policy recommendations are made.

SURVEY DESCRIPTION

The study covered five villages in Chachoengsao and three in Supanburi, Thailand, (Fig. 2) and six villages in Laguna and six in Iloilo, Philippines (Fig. 3). These provinces were chosen because of their high thresher use and concentration of rice thresher producers. They are also predominantly rice growing areas which have

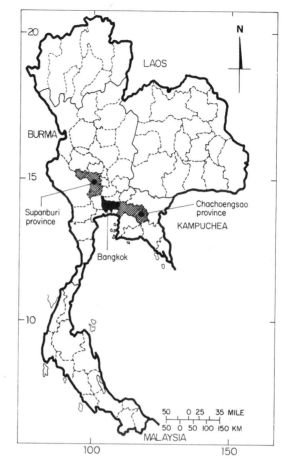

2. Location of study areas in Thailand, 1978-79.

widely adopted high yielding varieties. Other than the three rainfed villages in Iloilo, which were included for comparison, all have good irrigation. Land preparation is predominantly mechanized.

A total of 268 respondents in Thailand and 101 in the Philippines were interviewed in 1978-79. They were first grouped into thresher owners, thresher renters, and thresher nonusers (those employing only traditional methods). Samples were randomly selected from lists provided for each village. The sample size for each group is in Table 1. Nine thresher manufacturers in Thailand and six in the Philippines were also interviewed to provide supplementary information.

HISTORY OF MECHANICAL RICE THRESHING IN THAILAND AND PHILIPPINES

In 1975, the IRRI TH8 large axial-flow thresher started to replace buffalo and tractor treading in Thailand. In Laguna, the large IRRI TH8 axial-flow thresher began replacing hand beating in 1974 and was followed by the IRRI portable

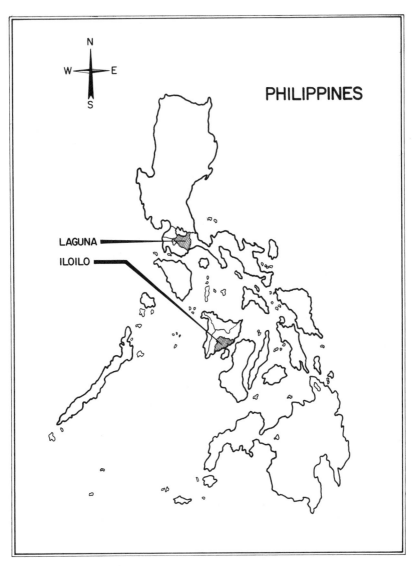

3. Location of study areas, Philippines, 1978-79.

thresher in 1975. Farmers preferred the larger machine. In Iloilo, the portable thresher started to replace foot treading in 1976. The introduction of threshers had considerable impact on labor (Table 2).

The rapid spread of threshers occurred in Thailand in 1976-78 and in the Philippines in 1976-78, some 2 to 3 years after introduction. Machines were purchased from manufacturers or dealers in the province; or sometimes from small village shops producing threshers by order. Manufacturer demonstrations and salesmen provided the first owners with thresher information. The first owners and users

Table 1. Distribution of respondents by survey area and group classification.

Country and province	Water source	Thresher owners (no.)	Thresher renters (no.)	Thresher nonusers (no.)				Total
				Buffalo treading	Tractor treading	Foot treading	Hand beating	
Thailand								
Chachoengsao	Irrigated	40	71	0	7	—	—	118
Supanburi	Irrigated	23	85	8	34	—	—	150
Total		63	156	8	41	—	—	268
Philippines								
Laguna	Irrigated	7	12	—	—	—	7	26
Iloilo	Irrigated	11	14	—	—	14	—	39
	Rainfed	5	16	—	—	15	—	36
Total		23	42	—	—	29	7	101

Table 2. Quantity of rice threshed and time used in threshing by different methods.

Method	Area[a]	Quantity of rice threshed (kg/man-day)	Time used (h/t)
Thailand			
Buffalo treading	Supanburi (8)	206	22
Tractor treading	Chachoengsao and Supanburi (37)	415	2.6
Large thresher	Chachoengsao and Supanburi (63)	752	0.7
Philippines			
Hand beating	Laguna (14)	182	1.6
Foot treading	Iloilo (24)	135	6.6
	Iloilo rainfed (20)	124	6.2
Large thresher	Laguna (5)	1070	1.1
Portable thresher	Laguna (5)	1136	1.6
	Iloilo (13)	1238	1.7
	Iloilo rainfed (5)	1316	1.6

[a]Values in parentheses are number of observations.

influenced other farmers. Most users in the survey areas traced their initial knowledge to seeing the machines on other farms.

For both countries, the major source of thresher innovation has been the IRRI Machinery Development Program.

Chachoengsao Province

In late 1975, a Bangkok manufacturer received, through the IRRI program, a blueprint and produced two IRRI-3 large axial-flow threshers. In early 1976, the Chaiwat Panich Shop in Chachoengsao produced 10 units. Each unit cost $342 and sold at $587. Threshing capacity was 1,000 kg/hour. Problems were encountered with the shaking screen and high separation loss.

At the end of 1976, while the IRRI-3 thresher was under review, Chaiwat Panich Shop and another manufacturer started producing the IRRI-5 axial-flow thresher. They produced 30 units. By mid-1977, other manufacturers and shops from outside and inside Chachoengsao had started production of these two models.

The portable thresher was introduced in the province in late 1977, but was not well accepted by farmers because of its lower capacity, so production terminated.

At present, there are six thresher manufacturers in Chachoengsao. The province uses 40% of all the rice threshers in the country.

Supanburi Province

Production in Supanburi started at the end of 1976, but only one firm is currently producing threshers. Statistics on use were unavailable.

Laguna Province

The first threshers to operate in Laguna, in 1974-75, were the IRRI large axial-flow thresher and the non-IRRI portable types. The non-IRRI designs are now used mainly on owners' farms. Custom work has been limited to the large IRRI type which has a cleaner output. In 1976, smaller portable types from IRRI were introduced and accepted, although the large type was still preferred.

The rapid spread of threshers in Laguna was enhanced by the location of Kaunlaran Industries Inc., the largest manufacturer of IRRI-designed threshers in the Philippines, some 10-20 km south of the study area. The area is traversed by the national road leading north to Manila and south to Los Baños. Three small machine shops also produce threshers. About 85% of the farmers in the area are thresher users (Fig. 4).

Iloilo Province
The first firm to produce the IRRI-designed portable thresher in Iloilo was Jamandre Industries Inc., which produced about 80 units in 1976. A medium-capacity shop followed in 1977 and another in 1978. The first three manufacturers, which sold about 700 units between 1976 and June 1979, were cooperators in the IRRI Machinery Development Program. At present, there are four cooperating manufacturers and about 10 other small manufacturers and welding and machine shops producing threshers in the province. They have produced an estimated 160 units. Seventy-five percent of farmers in the irrigated villages use threshers (Fig. 4) and all are the portable type.

FACTORS AFFECTING THRESHER ADOPTION

Besides international organizations and government agencies which served as innovators, and manufacturers who provided the linkage, several factors appeared to influence thresher adoption.

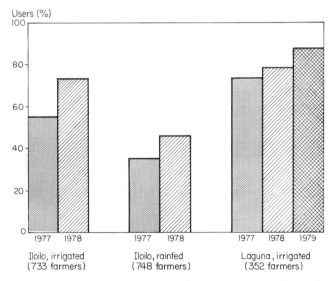

4. Thresher adoption and use in three irrigated and three rainfed Iloilo villages and six irrigated Laguna villages, Philippines, 1978-79.

Table 3. Profile of respondents.

| Item | Thailand | | | Philippines | | | | | |
| | | | | Irrigated | | | Rainfed | | |
	Owners	Renters	Nonusers	Owners	Renters	Nonusers	Owners	Renters	Nonusers
Respondents (no.)	63	156	49	18	26	21	5	16	15
Age (yr)	48	48	45	52	50	59	50	49	49
Education (yr)	4	4	4	6.3	4.7	5.0	5.1	6.7	5.4
Tenure (%)									
Landowner	70	65	86	56	38	57	60	60	67
Landless	30	35	14	44	62	43	40	40	33
Average farm size (ha)	8.9	6.0	7.5	5.1	2.1	1.8	4.4	2.7	2.4
Average yield (t/ha)	2.9	2.7	2.7	3.8	3.9	2.9	2.4	2.8	2.7

Characteristics of farmers and their farms

The average age of farmers in the survey ranged from 45 to 48 years in Thailand and 49 to 59 years in the Philippines (Table 3). Educational level was low in both countries with most respondents having 6 years of schooling or less. All Thai farmers reached the compulsory level of grade four. No significant differences were found in age or education among adopters and nonadopters at any of the sites. Farming experience was mostly from parents or friends.

There was no clear correlation between land ownership and thresher adoption. Farm size seemed to affect adoption in both countries; the average farm of thresher owners was larger than that of nonowners. Thresher owners tended to have a higher income net for threshing activities. Most thresher owners also owned power tillers before thresher acquisition.

High yielding varieties (HYV) such as RD7 and RD11 (Thailand) and IR36, IR38, and IR42 (Philippines) were commonly planted by all groups.

Most respondents participated in farmers' associations and extension programs, but there was no indication that such participation influenced thresher adoption.

Labor shortages consequent upon increases in cropping intensity

Manufacturers in Thailand and the Philippines started producing threshers when HYVs were already widespread. From the first year of manufacture to the present, production, sales, and use by farmers have been increasing.

Irrigation and HYVs made double-cropping possible. With the first crop usually harvested during the rainy months, the danger of grain spoilage was high. Since HYVs spoil and shatter more easily than traditional varieties, with a second crop to follow, more timely harvesting and threshing were required. The changes created a labor shortage during the peak harvesting and threshing months and led to changes in harvesting systems, including rapid adoption of mechanical threshers.

Time and cost savings

Time saved by using mechanical threshers can help farmers plant subsequent crops on time. There are also cost savings due to reduced losses (with the exception of tractor treading in Thailand) and the fact that meals are rarely served to workers.

The net cost savings of thresher use ranged from $2.70 in Thailand to $4.92 in the Philippines (Table 4). In Laguna and areas in Iloilo where meals were not served, the use of mechanical threshing involved extra costs. Hand beating in Laguna was fast and wages were low so that it was cheaper than the mechanical thresher.

Total variable costs for all threshing methods are in Table 5. Labor costs were the largest component.

Availability and cost of financing

For both countries, most threshers were bought with cash, using personal savings derived predominantly from farm income (Tables 6, 7). Availability and source of funds seemed to be an important factor determining thresher investment. In Thai-

Table 4. Net cost savings of switching from traditional methods of threshing to a rice thresher.[a]

Area	Traditional method	Cost ($/t)	Mechanical method	Cost ($/t)	Net cost saving ($/t)
Thailand					
Chachoengsao	Tractor treading	6.92	Large thresher	3.75	3.17
Supanburi	Tractor treading	7.49	Large thresher	4.79	2.70
	Buffalo treading	9.56	Large thresher	4.79	4.77
Philippines					
Laguna	Hand beating	7.47	Large thresher	9.31	−1.84
	Hand beating	7.47	Portable thresher	9.31	−1.84
Iloilo	Foot treading	6.69 (11.22)	Portable thresher	6.72	−0.03 (4.50)
Iloilo rainfed	Foot treading	6.71 (11.64)	Portable thresher	6.72	−0.01 (4.92)

[a]Numbers in parentheses are the net cost and net cost savings if traditional threshing includes meals.

Table 5. Cost of rice threshing by traditional method.[a]

Method	Time consumed (man or animal days/t)	Wage ($/day)	Cost ($/t)
Thailand			
Buffalo treading:			
Buffalo	2.75	0.25	0.67
Labor	4.85	1.83	8.90
Philippines			
Hand beating	5.49	1.36	7.47
Foot treading	7.43	0.90 (1.51)	6.69 (11.22)
Foot treading (Iloilo rainfed)	8.08	0.83 (1.44)	6.71 (11.64)

[a]Numbers in parentheses are costs including meals.

land, the maximum loan of about $300 from commercial banks and the Bank for Agriculture and Agricultural Cooperatives represented only 16% of the investment cost of threshers in 1979. So, potential buyers still had to use personal savings or borrow from private sources at 20-30% interest.

No agency in the Philippines specialized in the finance of thresher purchase; neither were farmers aware of possibilities. Interest rates of private moneylenders were most frequently 20-50% per annum, and sometimes as high as 80%.

Custom service
A very important factor affecting thresher adoption was the availability of customers for custom service. The field survey revealed the quantity of custom-threshed

Table 6. Sources of funds for rice thresher investment.[a]

Source	Thailand (63)	Philippines	
		Irrigated (24)	Rainfed (5)
Own cash (%)	69	83	60
Loans (%)	7	—	—
Both cash and loans (%)	24	17	40

[a]Values in parentheses indicate number of threshers.

Table 7. Sources of loans for rice thresher investment.

Source	Thailand		Philippines	
	Threshers (%)	Interest rate (%/yr)	Threshers (%)	Interest rate (%/yr)
Bank	74	12	17	12
Agricultural cooperatives	16	15	—	—
Private moneylenders	5	20-30	33	25-80
Relatives	5	0	17	0
Not specified	—	—	33	—

rice to be much higher than that threshed on owner farms. Custom services represented 89% of the total quantity of rice threshed in Chachoengsao, 83% in Supanburi, and 69% in Iloilo and Laguna. Custom services were also the main way threshers were available to farmers without their own machines.

Other reasons for adoption or nonadoption
In the Philippines, the main reasons for not using a thresher were small farms, low production, and harvesting in small quantities. The unavailability of custom services when needed was also important. Poor machine performance and dislike for threshers were rarely mentioned. In Thailand, some farmers preferred to thresh with tractors which they already owned. Others were not faced with labor shortage problems.

Many users and nonusers of threshers desired to own either a thresher or other machines. Table 8 shows that demand in Thailand was highest for power tillers, followed by that for rice threshers. In the Philippines, the demand for rice threshers was highest followed by that for mechanical blowers for grain cleaning. The major constraint to ownership was lack of capital.

PRIVATE COSTS AND BENEFITS OF THRESHER ADOPTION

The model
The methodology for estimating private costs and benefits of traditional and mechanical threshing methods in Thailand and the Philippines was as follows. For each method, the annual cash flows, defined as the difference between gross benefit from the investment and all input costs such as fuel, labor, and operating materials, were obtained. The net present value (NPV) for each investment was then estimated

using various discount rates and the standard formula (Branson 1975):

$$NPV = -C + \sum_{k=1}^{n} \frac{R_k}{(1+i)^k} + \frac{S_n}{(1+i)^n} \tag{1}$$

where:

C is the investment cost of the thresher, power engine attachment, and other complements;

R_k is the net income in period k;

S_n is the resale value at the end of period n; and

i is the discount rate.

For owners, benefits were assessed as gains from ownership and/or rental, whereas for renters they were gains from use.

The formula used for estimating these gains was:

$$R_t = NRF_t + NROF_t - MA_t + LS_t \tag{2}$$

where:

R_t is the gain in period t from thresher use as compared to traditional methods;

NRF is the net income obtained from on-farm use of a rice thresher in period t, which is equal to net cost savings per unit multiplied by the quantity threshed;

$NROF_t$ is the net income obtained from hiring out a thresher in period t, which is equal to the quantity threshed on a contract basis multiplied by the net thresher charge;

MA_t is the repair and maintenance expense for period t; and

LS_t is the benefit in terms of losses avoided as a result of using mechanical as opposed to traditional threshing in period t.

The terms $NROF_t$ and MA_t are zero (0) for renters because they cannot provide contract services and were not required to cover repair and maintenance costs.

The benefit-cost ratio (B:C) is the ratio between the NPV of benefits and the NPV of costs. It can be readily computed from the two formulas.

Table 8. Potential demand for farm machines.

Machine	Thailand (%)	Philippines	
		Iloilo and Laguna, irrigated (%)	Iloilo, rainfed (%)
Power tiller	22	3	8
Transplanter	13	–	–
Sprayer	17	–	–
Water pump	14	3	11
Combine	6	2	–
Rice Thresher	19	57	67
Winnower/blower	1	33	53
Dryer	–	3	–
Others[a]	9	0	3
None	25	35	14

[a]Including power engine, rice mill, trailer, and grass cutter.

Table 9. Sample data for investment analysis (1978 machines).

Description	Thailand		Philippines			
			Laguna		Iloilo	
	Chachoengsao	Supanburi	Large	Portable	Irrigated	Rainfed
Machines (no.)	15	21	3	2	6	3
Purchase price ($)	1343	1902	2136	837	748	789
Resale value of machine ($)	1185	1634	–	837	741	781
On-farm threshing (t/yr)	45	41	18	19	13	12
Off-farm threshing (t/yr)	312	339	109	11	120	56
Rice thresher charge ($/t)	2.06	2.96	4.62	5.05	3.85	3.85
Variable costs of thresher operation ($/t)	3.75	4.79	9.31	9.31	6.72	6.72
Threshing wage (% of output)	–	–	7	7	5.5	5.5
Paddy price ($/t)	–	–	133	133	122	122
Wage rates for traditional threshing ($/day)	1.83	1.67	1.36	1.36	.90	.83
Average paddy yields (t/ha)	–	–	3.5	3.5	3.5	2.6
Threshing time (man-d/t)	–	–	0.93	0.88	0.81	0.76
Variable cost of traditional threshing ($/t)	6.92	7.49	7.47	7.47	6.69	6.71
Maintenance cost of machine ($)	38	38	–	25	22	23
Gains involved in change to new method (% of output)	–0.72	–0.72	5.7	6.0	0.3	0.3

Data

The survey provided data on mean costs and returns of changes in threshing technology. Table 9 shows performance information for 1978, covering machines purchased during that year (unless otherwise stated). Similar data sets for the other years are reported in Juarez and Pathnopas (1981). Subsequent analyses combine each year's information with data relating to output to obtain a profile of annual returns.

Analyses and results

Two types of analysis were carried out. First, the survey data were used to construct historic cost and benefit streams for past investments in order to analyze the outcomes of these investments. Past investments included purchase and use of contracting services. Second, with 1978 data as the information available to a potential investor in 1978, the profitability of future investments was investigated.

Table 10. Net present 1978 value[a] at different discount rates by investment year.

Site	Discount rate (%)	Net present value by investment year (1978 $)				
		1974	1975	1976	1977	1978
Thailand						
				Large thresher		
Chachoengsao	12		940	1937	1356	555
	15		894	1925	1341	555
	25		715	1877	1284	555
Supanburi	12		–	–	1743	747
	15		–	–	1722	747
	25		–	–	1652	747
Philippines						
				Large thresher		
Laguna	12	–1732	–500	1357		
	15	–2068	–682	1289		
	25	–3391	–1357	1051		
	30	–8420	–3610	340		
				Portable thresher		
	12		1154			143
	15		1185			143
	25		1297			143
	50		1590			143
Iloilo	12				296 (456)	436 (497)
	15				280 (443)	436 (497)
	25				232 (402)	436 (497)
	50				109 (300)	436 (497)
Iloilo rainfed	12				495 (568)	189 (247)
	15				486 (560)	189 (247)
	25				454 (531)	189 (247)
	50				375 (461)	189 (247)

[a]Numbers in parentheses are the net present values if traditional threshing includes meals.

The costs and returns of investment were transformed into 1978 values using discount rates ranging from 12% to 50%.

Purchase of a thresher before or during 1978. Table 10 shows the NPV by investment year for farmers who purchased threshers before or during 1978. With the exception of early adopters of large threshers in Laguna, the NPV were positive at all discount rates. In addition, NPV appeared to decline with later adoption. The exceptions seemed to be the earliest adopters in Chachoengsao, Iloilo irrigated, and the large thresher adopters in Laguna. The reasons were that many of the earliest adopters threshed very low levels of rice (Iloilo irrigated, Laguna, Chachoengsao), investment costs were high (Iloilo irrigated), and the two earliest adopters in Chachoengsao were not interested in providing custom services.

The pattern appeared to be one of difficulties with high cost equipment and lack of output in the early years when there were very positive benefits to be gained, followed by a decline in benefits as machines became more widespread and competition increased.

Use of custom service before or during 1978. Farmers who do not own a thresher can gain some benefits from net cost and the grain loss savings by switching from traditional threshing to custom use of threshers. Maximum and minimum gains are in Table 11. In each classification, the smaller gains were in Supanburi Province, where cultivated areas in wet and dry seasons were relatively smaller than in Chachoengsao. In the Philippines, gains were higher in the irrigated areas, where threshers substituted for hand beating and traditional threshing included meals.

The range of gains per farm provides no guidance as to whether large farms benefit more than small ones. Results according to farm size are in Table 12. With the exception of Laguna, small farms gained relatively more per hectare by switching to a thresher than either the medium or large farms. The net cost saving, the losses saved, and the yield were all larger on the smaller farms.

Purchase of a thresher after 1978. A single discount rate was used to simplify the analysis of investing in a rice thresher in 1979. Possible rates were the bank and agricultural cooperative rate of 12-14% and the local moneylender rate of 20-50%. Because the rates charged by moneylenders tended to more adequately reflect the opportunity cost of money, the modal value of 25% was selected for subsequent discussion.

The machine life-span of 20 years was chosen arbitrarily. Although the machine might still be functional after 20 years, a newer type with a better performance would doubtless be available.

Other variables, such as labor cost, future prices of petroleum products, and maintenance costs affect the present value of thresher investments. Sensitivity analyses were done to determine the degree to which costs changes would affect profitability. Labor costs in Thailand were estimated to increase at 3.2%/annum. This is close to the 3.4%/annum growth rate of real GNP for 1965-77. Labor costs for the Philippines were held constant at the 1978 level. It is difficult to estimate future real prices for petroleum products although they will almost inevitably rise. A number of rates of increase were therefore simulated, although the effects of only three (10, 30, and 50%/annum) are presented in this study. Similarly, the rate of

Table 11. Maximum, minimum, and average gains of using a thresher or traditional methods of threshing.

Threshing method	Average net cost saving ($)	Average gains from losses saved ($)	Total gains ($/farm) Average	Maximum	Minimum
Chachoengsao, Thailand		*Large thresher*			
Tractor treading	114	-32	82	123	48
Supanburi, Thailand					
Tractor treading	48	-16	32	36	27
Buffalo treading	84	-12	72	83	63
Laguna, Philippines		*Large thresher*			
Hand beating	-36	149	113	262	8
		Portable thresher			
Hand beating	-83	156	120	278	9
Iloilo, Philippines					
Foot treading	-0.3 (40)[a]	3.3	3.0 (43)	9.2 (129)	1.1 (16)
Foot treading	-0.1 (42)	3.2	3.0 (45)	6.0 (86)	1.2 (17)

[a]Numbers in parentheses are values if traditional threshing includes meals.

Table 12. Gains from using a thresher or traditional methods of threshing, by farm size.

Site, threshing method	Total gains ($/ha)		
	Large[a]	Medium[b]	Small[c]
Chachoengsao, Thailand			
Tractor treading	17	11	19
Supanburi, Thailand			
Tractor treading	12	9	15
Buffalo treading	23	19	29
Laguna, Philippines			
Hand beating	34	27	18
Hand beating	36	28	19
Iloilo, Philippines			
Foot treading	1.1	1.2	1.5
	(16)	(16)	(21)
Iloilo rainfed			
Foot treading	1.0	1.0	1.5
	(14)	(14)	(21)

[a] > 4.8 ha in Thailand and > 3.0 ha in the Philippines. [b] 2.4-4.8 ha in Thailand and 1.0-3.0 ha in the Philippines. [c] < 2.4 ha in Thailand and < 1.0 ha in the Philippines.

Table 13. Returns to thresher purchase over 20 years.[a]

Location	Present value of 20-year income stream ($)	Benefit-cost ratio
Chachoengsao	2794	2.08
Supanburi	4118	2.17
Laguna		
Large thresher	2158	1.01
Portable thresher	574	0.69
Iloilo	1758 (1998)	2.35 (2.67)

[a]Numbers in parentheses are values if meals are included for traditional threshing.

increase of maintenance costs as machines age is difficult to forecast, so analyses were undertaken with 10 and 40% annual growth rates.

Returns to thresher purchase if all variables are held constant at 1978 levels are in Table 13.

In Chachoengsao, Supanburi, and Iloilo, threshers were profitable, with a B:C of over 2.0; in Laguna, with similar rates of output, only the large thresher showed a B:C greater than unity and then only after 20 years.

Table 14 shows the results of the sensitivity analyses. In Thailand, where threshers substituted for tractor treading, an increase in petroleum product prices increased the profitability of threshers. In the Philippines, where threshers replaced foot treading and hand beating, an increase in petroleum costs decreased the thresher profitability.

Table 14. Benefit-cost ratios (B:C) based on various sets of assumptions at 25% discount rate and a project life of 20 years.

Site	Machine	Benefit-cost ratio					
Chachoengsao	Large thresher	2.03	1.47	2.56	1.62	6.74	4.94
Supanburi		2.03	1.22	1.94	1.31	4.42	3.18
Laguna	Large thresher	0.37	0.18	0.31	0.17	0.25	0.15
	Portable thresher	0.40	0.23	0.33	0.21	0.27	0.19
Iloilo	Portable thresher[a]	0.23	0.18	0.21	0.16	0.18	0.14
		(0.63)	(0.41	(0.51)	(0.37)	(0.41)	(0.33)
	Assumptions: (% annual increase)						
Fuel		10	10	30	30	50	50
Maintenance		10	40	10	40	10	40

[a]Values in parentheses are B:C when traditional threshing includes meals.

Increasing maintenance costs reduces the annual cash flow significantly. In Thailand, however, the B:C was still greater than unity even with a 40% increase in maintenance.

CONCLUSIONS

The adoption of mechanized threshing in Thailand and the Philippines has been rapid over the past 2-4 years. There has been a simultaneous rapid adoption of modern varieties in response to the installation and expansion of irrigation facilities.

The first rice thresher adoption in Thailand was of an IRRI-designed large axial-flow type in Chachoengsao in 1975. In the Philippines the first owner in 1974, from Laguna, also acquired a large type from IRRI. It was followed later by the portable type non-IRRI designs in 1975 and the portable IRRI design in 1976. In both countries, use of these machines has spread widely in areas which are relatively well irrigated and double-cropped. The original source of the innovation was IRRI, which supported production by local manufacturers. The first buyers were predominantly large farmers. Custom services provided by these owners for extra income became so common that use of the machine spread rapidly even to nonowners. In the Philippines, 75% of the farmers in the irrigated villages surveyed in 1978 were thresher users as were 45% in the rainfed area. A follow-up survey in 1981 found 100% users.

Contracting, rather than cooperative ownership, is the main way in which machines have been made available to farmers lacking the capital to buy. In Thailand, the average custom charge in 1978 was $2.5-3.4/t, paid in cash. In the Philippines, the contract charge was paid in kind at 5.5-7% of gross production. The rate in Thailand covered only the cost of the semiskilled thresher operators fuel and oil costs, transportation, and machine service charges. The customers had to find an additional 5-6 laborers to assist with threshing. In the Philippines, these laborers were included in the rate.

Thresher owners gained from use on their own farm and from providing custom services. The estimated NPV indicated a high profitability for past investments.

Expectations of profitability for future investments were also high in Thailand. In the Philippines, however, future investments were less favorable because the number of threshers in use is large and opportunities for custom work are limited.

The two main benefits for users were the net cost savings and the gains from avoided losses. In Thailand, farmers who switched from traditional to mechanical threshing obtained a net cost saving of $2.70-3.17/t, but lost 0.54-0.72% of the grain threshed. In the Philippines, switching from traditional to mechanical threshing gave negative net cost savings of $0.01-1.84/t if meals were not provided for traditional threshing, but positive savings of $4.50-4.92/t with meals. Losses amounting from 3-6% of the gross threshed rice were avoided with machine use. Time saved by using the thresher was valued at the prevailing wage rate and incorporated into the costs saved. Such time may be used for better farm management, increased leisure activities, or some other income-generating activities and could have a higher value. The NPV of total benefits for thresher renters and users ranged from $9-19/ha for medium farms in Thailand and from $1.0-28/ha for those in the Philippines. The average gains ranged from $32-82/farm in Thailand and $3-120/farm in the Philippines.

Increases in fuel costs would make thresher investment in Thailand more profitable because of the relatively higher fuel consumption of tractors as compared to threshers. In the Philippines, increases in fuel costs would make thresher investment less profitable because traditional threshing does not use fuel. As maintenance costs increased, thresher investment became less profitable.

Even though the net benefits are positive, investment in and use of threshers may be constrained by institutional factors such as availability of credit, farm size, and availability of customers for custom services.

REFERENCES CITED

Branson, W. H. 1975. Macroeconomic theory and policy. 2d ed. Harper and Row, New York.

Juarez, F., and R. Pathnopas. 1981. A comparative analysis of thresher adoption and utilization in Thailand and the Philippines. The Consequences of Small Rice Farm Mechanization Project. Working Paper 28.

Khan, A. U. 1971. Harvesting and threshing of paddy. A paper presented at the 1971 International Rice Research Conference, IRRI, Los Baños, Laguna, Philippines.

Rasanond, S., V. Veerayankul, M. Congrakultien, and J. Apibunyopas. 1977. A survey of the IRRI axial-flow thresher efficiency compared with the traditional methods of threshing. Report, Faculty of Economics and Business Administration, Agribusiness Management Program, Kasetsart University. (unpubl.)

Sison, W. M., B. C. Sarmiento, and C. C. Dacumos. 1977. Comparative study and test evaluation of village type rice threshers. Paper on Post-Harvest Rice Technology, National Grains Authority, Philippines. (unpubl.)

LABOR USE PATTERNS AND MECHANIZATION OF RICE POSTHARVEST PROCESSING IN BANGLADESH

J. U. Ahmed

In Bangladesh, the economic necessity for farm level mechanization of rice processing does not appear strong. This may be attributed to the low labor requirement of traditional methods, extensive use of low cost, female family labor, and the low level of
postharvest losses. The analysis revealed that average food loss per
farm, due to wet season drying constraints, was well below the level
at which using small-scale dryers for supplementary mechanical
drying would be economic. In contrast, custom hullers, which have
high labor productivity, are widely used. They were found to have
caused some employment and income imbalances among the rural
poor, and suitable programs are required to alleviate these
problems.

Rice is the principal food grain crop in Bangladesh, accounting for 75% of total
cropland. In 1979-80, Bangladesh produced 12.5 million t of rice and 0.8 million t of
wheat (Bangladesh Bureau of Statistics 1980). Hence domestic production covers
about 90% of the current requirements of 14.7 million t. Rice production is frag-
mented into small family farms with an average size of 1.1 ha (Bangladesh Bureau of
Statistics 1979). The most important features underlying the rice postharvest system
are the low proportion (10-15%) of marketed surplus (Farruk 1970, Greeley 1980a)
and the dominance of traditional processing methods with extremely low capital-
labor ratios.

There are two opposing views on the necessity of mechanizing postharvest
processing at the farm level (BCSIR 1980, CIRDAP 1981). Technologists and
development assistance groups in donor countries frequently argue that postharvest
mechanization may help reduce the food grain deficit in Bangladesh by bringing
down the level of postharvest loss. Wimberly (1974) has claimed a quantity loss of
20% and Karim (1979) suggested a quality loss of 50-100%. They also argue that
mechanization may release labor for more profitable alternative employment. The
second view is that postharvest losses are not high enough to force the farmers to

Bangladesh Agricultural University.

adopt alternative technologies (Huq and Greeley 1980, Ahmed 1981b). Moreover, it has been argued that improved postharvest technologies may adversely affect rural employment and income distribution (Ahmed 1981a).

Both views recognize that the labor saving potential of improved postharvest technologies provides a major source of increased income. To date, field surveys on postharvest processing have emphasized largely loss assessment rather than labor use patterns under alternative technologies. So, it is difficult to draw inferences on the labor saving potential of improved postharvest technologies.

In Bangladesh, where labor is relatively abundant and traditional processing methods require little labor, low postharvest losses limit the potential of small-scale mechanization. However, the superior labor productivity of rural custom hulling, compared to traditional husking, has attracted substantial private investment. The imbalances in rural employment and income distribution caused by such technological change are examined.

The major emphasis of the paper is on threshing, drying, and husking (the three operations for which labor requirements and use of hired labor are hypothesized to be most affected by mechanization). The rate of adoption and expansion of modern labor saving technologies was hypothesized to be positively correlated with labor requirement and the use of hired labor in these operations. The consequences of postharvest mechanization on employment and income distribution were investigated with particular reference to the expansion of the huller mills, the only commercial level technology in the rural postharvest sector.

Data were from a field survey of 76 randomly selected households in the vicinities of two huller mills in Shimla and Padurbari villages, Mymensingh. The mills were commissioned in 1979 when the area came under the rural electrification program. Additional data were from a survey of 80 farms conducted in 1980 in Boyra and Sutiakhali villages, Mymensingh. The purpose of this survey was to investigate the problems of postharvest processing of aus rice, an early wet season crop for which drying problems are generally experienced.

SUPPLY AND DISPOSAL OF RICE IN THE SAMPLE HOUSEHOLDS

The type and sequence of postharvest operations for rice are largely influenced by its intended use. However, emergencies such as the need for immediate consumption, forced sale, or postharvest technology constraints may force farmers to change. Before analyzing the mode of rice disposal, some socioeconomic characteristics of the sample households are presented in Table 1 because they have considerable influence on rice disposal.

Farming in the study area is characterized by small landholdings and operational areas. Forty-nine percent of the sample households hired out labor and could be classified as poor. The relative depth of poverty in the poor households may be gauged by the size of landholding, dominance of rented land in the total operational area, extent of hiring out of permanent labor and female labor, and the proportion of family income derived from female labor. By all of these criteria, those employed by farmers were the poorest.

Considerable differences were also found in the pattern of supply and disposal of

Table 1. Characteristics of the sample households in Shimla and Padurbari, Mymensingh, Bangladesh.

Characteristics	Poor families			Nonpoor families
	Employed by producer farmers	Paddy processing groups	Permanent laborer in rice mills	
Sample households (no.)	24	11	2	39
Owned land (ha/household)	0.065	0.138	0.085	1.202
Mortgaged-in land (ha/household)	—	—	—	0.004
Rented-in land (ha/household)	0.036	0.137	—	0.113
Mortgaged-out land (ha/household)	0.004	0.012	—	0.004
Rented-out land (ha/household)	—	0.032	0.028	0.158
Operated land per family (ha/household)	0.097	0.227	0.057	1.158
Households hiring in labor (%)	—	—	—	90
Households hiring in postharvest female labor (%)	—	—	—	54
Households hiring out labor (%)	100	100	100	—
Households hiring out permanent labor (%)	62	10	100	—
Households hiring out female labor (%)	71	38	50	—
Earnings from female labor (%)	33	6	11	—

rice between the various categories (Table 2). Overall, own production was the largest source (53%). By category, the nonpoor household received only 0.5% of their rice from wages and purchases, the poor received 25% and the poorest 87%.

Major ways of disposing of rice were home consumption (69%), sale (17%), and seed (6%). The marketed surplus varied greatly between household categories. In-kind payment to laborers and barter for household goods together accounted for 5% of the total and usually consisted of low quality grain which, because it is transferred to users with lower per capita availability, probably results in a net increase in utility. A loss assessment survey of 80 households in Boyra and Sutiakhali (Ahmed 1981b) indicated that only 1% of the gross yield deteriorated qualitatively by molding and germination. A similar low level of qualitative loss was reported by Greeley (1981). Farmers appear to reduce or eliminate qualitative loss by disposing of affected grains through in-kind payment or barter.

Postharvest processing consists of physical handling of the crop from field to farm, stacking, threshing, winnowing, soaking, parboiling, drying, storing, husking, polishing, cooking, and other forms of final processing.

The actual combination and sequence of operations vary widely depending on end use, crop season, and farm resources. The field survey conducted in Boyra and Sutiakhali identified five major sequences of rice processing (Table 3) and nine

Table 2. Supply and disposal of rice in sample households, 1979-80.

Supply, disposal	Employed farmers[a] (kg)	Rice processing groups (kg)	Nonpoor families (kg)
Supply			
Carried over	9	13	39
Own production	193	506	3,460
Tenant's share	–	369	206
Landlord's share	–	90	298
Purchased[b]	477	202	19
Borrowed/received back	6	14	11
Wage	238	135	–
Gift	9	24	27
Total	933	1,353	4,059
Disposal			
Seed	9	93	385
Sale[b]	8	29	1,269
Payment in kind for			
Postharvest labor	–	–	121
Other labor	–	–	158
Barter for goods	4	5	107
Loaned/repaid	6	14	11
Gift	–	4	25
Home consumption[c]	899	1,178	1,845
Carried over	7	30	139
Total	933	1,353	4,059
Meals taken in employers house[d]	535	137	–

[a]Includes two respondents working as permanent laborers at the mills. [b]Excludes transactions for the processing business. [c]Includes meals taken by laborers. [d]Assumes 0.23 kg rice/meal.

Table 3. Distribution of aus output by major sequences of postproduction operations by farm size.

Sequence[a]	Distribution (%) of output by farm size			
	<1 ha	1-1.99 ha	≥2 ha	All
Parboiling, drying, husking for immediate consumption	59	31	24	36
Parboiling, drying, storage for future husking	15	26	28	24
Drying, storage for consumption	12	12	11	12
Drying, storage for seed	7	12	8	9
Drying, storage for sale	0	5	19	9

[a]All sequences commenced with cutting, carrying, threshing 1 and 2.

minor sequences. Most of the rice intended for consumption was parboiled. Mainly because of labor shortage more than one-third of the parboiled rice was dried and kept in storage for future husking. Some farmers felt that storage improved milling quality. Rice also was frequently dried and stored for several weeks before parboiling due to a fuel shortage and the belief that storage improves the quality of the rice, particularly of high yielding varieties (HYV).

The sequence of operations and disposal pattern varied according to farm size and rice variety. The larger farms produced a higher proportion of marketed surplus. The proportion of grains sold or given away in repayment of loans, advancement of loans, in-kind payment to laborers, or as barter was higher for HYVs than for local varieties (Ahmed et al 1980).

LABOR REQUIREMENT FOR TRADITIONAL POSTHARVEST PROCESSING

The labor requirement for postharvest processing represents 30-33% of labor use (Ahmed 1981a) and 25% of all agricultural employment (Greeley 1980b). Information on labor use in individual postharvest operations is however limited, the only sources being Abdullah and Zeidenstein (1977), Arrens and Van Beurden (1977), Harriss (1979), Sattar (1975), and Von Harder (1975). All sources suffer from the major drawback that estimates were based on personal communications rather than surveys and therefore seem to be uniformly "standardized" (Ahmed 1981a).

Table 4 shows the labor requirement for postharvest paddy processing in Shimla and Padurbari. The average requirement by traditional methods was 36.7 mandays/t. The requirement was higher in the aus and boro season because of rain. The labor, almost entirely female, required for husking was 52% of total postharvest employment. Threshing, which is done almost exclusively by males, accounted for 14% of the labor. Winnowing, soaking, parboiling, drying, and husking were done predominantly by women who contributed 86% of the labor for processing.

Reduction of labor costs through modernization of the prehusking operations is limited because the labor required for these operations, using traditional technology, is low and the opportunity cost of the labor, female family members, is also very low. In contrast, there are estimated to be 1,000 hullers in Bangladesh (Ahmed 1981a) and the number is estimated to be increasing at 380/annum (Salahuddin 1980). The

Table 4. Labor requirements for postharvest rice processing by traditional methods.

Operation	Labor requirements (man-day/t) by season				Hired labor (%)
	Aman	Boro	Aus	Average	
Threshing	4.6	5.4	5.9	5.1	25
Winnowing[a] (3 times)	4.0	4.0	4.0	4.0	14
Soaking	0.8	0.8	0.8	0.8	–
Parboiling	3.8	3.8	3.8	3.8	14
Drying	2.9	5.1	2.7	4.0	14
Husking and polishing	19.0	19.0	19.0	19.0	32
All operations	35.1	38.1	38.6	36.7	25

[a]One winnowing after threshing and two after husking and polishing.

reason for this rapid adoption is the high labor productivity compared to husking by traditional methods. An estimated 23-36% of total production is currently husked by mills and hullers (Bangladesh Bureau of Statistics 1979).

The survey in Shimla and Padurbari also revealed that, although 46% of the sample families hired in labor for farm work, only 28% hired in female labor for postharvest processing. So, improved technologies may reduce the use of family labor rather than hired labor.

FARM-LEVEL DEMAND FOR MODERN POSTHARVEST TECHNOLOGIES

Rice hullers are most popular for mechanized postharvest technology. Next are the Comilla-type pedal threshers, of which about 4,000 units are in use. Small-scale crop dryers (natural draft, bellows-powered, and solar) have not been adopted. Labor productivity and return on investment appear to be the major factors influencing the rate of adoption of the technologies. The annual profit and rate of return on investment for a custom mill, as calculated from data gathered by Harriss (1979) on 14 custom mills, are $1,130 and 70%, respectively.

The labor productivity of the mills was 5.6 t/man-day as compared to 0.2 t/man-day for traditional methods. In the case of small, natural draft dryers, labor productivity was less than 100 kg/man-day compared to 250-500 kg man-day for traditional methods. The nature of the wet season drying problem also makes it unlikely that small-scale dryers would be economic.

Pedal threshers were generally confined to big farmers with a labor constraint. Group interviews with users in the Bangladesh Agricultural University Extension Project area revealed that the major reasons for their use were higher labor productivity and suitability for special circumstances, such as inside the farmhouse during rainy periods. Custom milling services are widely used, but the high investment cost precludes farmer ownership. Finally, the small-scale natural draft dryers under trial in the project area require relatively low investment, but there are three preconditions for farmer demand:

    1. Increasing the efficiency of the dryer to lower the cost per unit dried;

    2. A high threat of molding and sprouting due to bad weather; and

    3. Availability of fuel.

Figure 1 shows break-even points between costs and gains of using small-scale dryers, under various conditions, based on the results of a postharvest loss assessment survey of aus in the dryer trial site (Ahmed 1981b). The survey showed a loss in value of $25.70/t affected by molding and sprouting due to drying constraints. The fixed costs of dryer construction and installation were conservatively estimated at $3.60/annum by spreading the total cost of $36 over 10 years and ignoring the opportunity cost of the investment. Fuel costs were estimated at $3.20/t and labor cost was excluded because family labor was sufficient. Assuming mechanical drying will supplement open sun-drying only during periods of more than 3 days continuous rain, the break-even point was estimated at 160 kg/annum threatened with molding and sprouting. Including the opportunity cost of capital at 10-15% would increase this break-even point significantly. In the study area, an average of only 15.3 kg of aus/farm was affected by molding and sprouting due to bad weather.

The break-even point would be improved either by increasing dryer efficiency when the cost line will shift from TC_1 to TC_2, or if there was an increased threat of food loss when the total gain line would move from TG_1 to TG_2. Also, where food loss occurs with boro rice, part of which is harvested during wet season, the quantity requiring mechanical drying will be larger, and the economics of the dryer will improve.

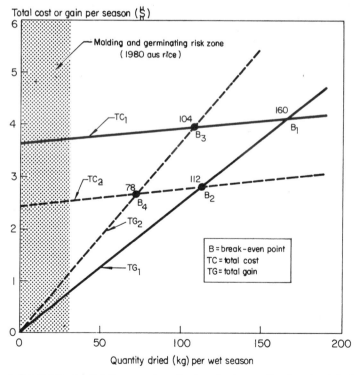

1. Break-even points between costs and gains of using small-scale natural draft dryers on trial in Bangladesh.

Under the prevailing small farming conditions in Bangladesh, the commercial scope for mechanical dryers is at government procurement depots and milling centers where the scale of operation and risk of loss may be higher. However, if dryer efficiency can be increased, they may become economic for some larger farmers.

Table 5. Employment for husking.

Information	Area without huller mill	Area with huller mill	
		Before	After
Number of farms	80	76	76
Farms hiring labor (%)	41	53	46
Farms reporting husking by hired labor (%)	41	49	46
Farms reporting use of male labor in husking (%)	19	21	9
Farms using mill (%)	–	–	37
Paddy husked by hired labor[a] (%)	24	32	16
Paddy husked at mill[a] (%)	–	–	29
Paddy husked by family labor[a] (%)	76	68	55

[a]Excludes rice for processing business.

Table 6. Effect of huller mill on two categories of rural poor.[a]

Effect of huller mills	Employed by farmers	Engaged as processing group
On size of employment (no.)	24	11
Increased (%)	13	9
Decreased (%)	83	27
Unchanged (%)	4	64
On terms of employment		
Changed from daily or contract labor to permanent labor (%)	63	–
Changed from permanent to daily or contract labor (%)	13	27
Unchanged (%)	25	73
On wage rate		
Increased (%)	–	–
Decreased (%)	79	18
Unchanged (%)	21	82
On net income		
Increased (%)	–	100
Decreased (%)	88	–
Unchanged (%)	13	–

[a]Of the 76 farmers interviewed 37 were employed by others. Two of these were employed at the huller mills and have been excluded.

EMPLOYMENT AND INCOME EFFECT OF MODERNIZED POSTHARVEST TECHNOLOGY

The impact of custom hullers on employment and income distribution may be examined using the data from the Shimla-Padurbari household survey. The introduction of mechanical hullers seemed not to have significantly reduced the number of hired labor users (Table 5). Although 37% of the sample households used huller mills, only 29% of their rice was husked at the mills. After mill establishment, hired labor dropped from 32% to 16% and family labor from 68% to 55%.

The employment and income distribution impacts of huller mills on the categories of rural poor engaged in processing differ (Table 6). Those employed by farmers have been displaced most. Hiring rural poor for husking tended to shift from casual to permanent employment (more than 3 months) (Tables 6 and 7), and that could have had a positive impact on the number and security of those employed. However, such a shift was associated with a decrease in the hourly wage rate because permanent employees traditionally work almost twice as long as casual laborers.

Three different wage rates for female husking labor were collected: the rate for permanent labor per year, the rate for daily labor, and the rate for contract labor per unit of output. Annual rates varied widely among areas and periods depending on the capacity of the laborer, the privileges enjoyed, and employer generosity. On the average, however, wage rates declined after mill introduction, and rates were lower in the area with mills than in areas without. Considering the 19% increase in the rural cost of living over this period, there has been a large fall in real wages. The same is true for daily and contract rates.

There was no significant difference in the daily wage rate for female husking labor between the area with mills and that without, although the daily rates had decreased slightly in the mill areas after they began operation. The largest decline was in hourly

Table 7. Employment terms and wage rates for female huskers.

	Area without rice mill	Area with rice mill	
		before	after
Total no. of farms	80	76	76
No. hired for husking	33	37	35
Permanent labor	13	20	22
Day labor	20	34	13
Wage rates for permanent labor[a]			
Cash ($/annum)	120-180	114-150	108-138
Meals[b] (no./day)	2.5	2.5	2.5
In kind[c] ($/annum)	2.4-3.6	2.4	2.4
Wage rates for day labor[a]			
Cash ($/day)	0.30-0.36	0.30-0.42	0.30-0.36
Meals[b] (no./day)	2.5	2.5	2.5
Contract wage rate[ad]			
($/t)	14.5-16.0	12.9-14.5	11.3

[a]Based on rates quoted by employers and laborers. [b]Valued at $0.12/meal. [c]Mainly clothes and poor quality rice. [d]Plus husk.

Table 8. Costs and returns to family labor in small-scale rice processing using alternative milling technologies.

Costs, returns	Traditional husking ($/day)	Husked at custom mill ($/day)
Costs		
Purchase of rice	6.30	18.90
Fuel for parboiling	0.12	0.24
Transport	0.12	0.24
Husking, milling	—[a]	1.08
Interest on operating capital	1.00	0.18
Total	6.60	20.64
Returns		
Sale of rice	7.29	21.86
Husk, bran, and broken rice	0.12	0.36
Total	7.41	22.22
Return to family labor	0.81	1.58

[a]Husked by family members.

contract rates. The only rural poor deriving large benefits from custom mills were the operators of small-scale paddy processing businesses (Table 8). Before mill introduction, a processing family with one working woman could husk 37 kg of dried rice/day and simultaneously parboil and dry another 37 kg for husking the next day. After introduction, all of the families changed to custom hulling and did more parboiling and drying. Using traditional technology, the return to family labor in processing was 22-34% higher than the daily wage rate for husking. Using custom hulling, the return to family labor was 139-163% higher than the daily wage rate. So with some operating capital for purchasing rice, many of the rural poor displaced by custom mills could probably earn a larger income by operating independent processing businesses using mill services. In addition, other activities such as beef fattening, milk cow rearing, and poultry may provide means for displaced laborers to earn an income. Policy makers involved in the rehabilitation of this displaced labor force need to investigate each of these alternatives.

REFERENCES CITED

Abdullah, T., and S. Zeidenstein. 1977. Bari-based postharvest operations and livestock care. Ford Foundation Rep. 48. Dacca.

Ahmed, J. U. 1981a. Impact of new paddy postharvest technology on the rural poor in Bangladesh. Paper presented at the seminar on Rural Technology, Rural Institutions and the Rural Poorest sponsored by the CIRDAP and IDS/Sussex February 2-5, 1981. Comilla, Bangladesh.

Ahmed, J. U. 1981b. Economics of traditional postharvest technology under small-scale farming: the case of paddy in a selected area of Bangladesh. Forthcoming report for the A/D/C, New York.

Ahmed, J. U. et al. 1980. Effects of farm size and tenancy on post-production loss as estimated by farmers: the case of aus paddy. Paper presented at the Post-production Workshop on Food Grains, The Bangladesh Council of Scientific and Industrial Research, December 12-14, 1980. Dacca.

Arens, J., and J. Van Beurden. 1977. Jhagrapur: poor peasants and women in a village in Bangladesh. Third World Publications, Birmingham.

Bangladesh Bureau of Statistics. 1979. Statistical yearbook of Bangladesh 1979. Ministry of Planning, Dacca.

Bangladesh Bureau of Statistics. 1980. Monthly statistical bulletin of Bangladesh. 9, 12 (December 1980).

BCSIR (The Bangladesh Council of Scientific and Industrial Research). 1980. Proceedings of Post-production Workshop on Food Grains, December 12-14, 1980. Dacca.

CIRDAP (Center on Integrated Rural Development for Asia and the Pacific). 1981. Proceedings of the seminar on Rural Technology, Rural Institutions and the Rural Poorest, February 2-5. Comilla, Bangladesh.

Farruk, M. O. 1970. The structure and performance of the rice marketing system in East Pakistan. Occas. pap. 31. Department of Agricultural Economics, Cornell University.

Greeley, M. 1980a. Rural technology, rural institutions and the rural poorest. Discussion paper. IDS/Sussex.

Greeley, M. 1980b. Farm-level post-harvest food losses: the myth of the soft third option. Paper presented at the Post-production Workshop on Food Grains, BCSIR, December 12-14, 1980. Dacca.

Greeley, M. 1981. Rural technology, rural institutions and the rural poorest: the case of rice processing in Bangladesh. Paper presented at the seminar on Rural Technology, Rural Institutions and the Rural Poorest sponsored by the CIRDAP and IDS/Sussex, February 2-5, 1981. Comilla, Bangladesh.

Harriss, B. 1979. Post harvest rice processing systems in rural Bangladesh: technology, economics and employment. Bangladesh J. Agric. Econ. 2(1):23-50.

Huq, A. K. F., and M. Greeley. 1980. Rice in Bangladesh: an empirical analysis of farm level food losses in five post-production operations. Paper presented at the Grains Post-Harvest Workshop. SEARCA, Kuala Lumpur.

Karim, A. M. A. 1979. Extent of loss of boro paddy during post-harvest operation. Agri-Varsity Extension Project, Mymensingh, Publ. 10.

Salahuddin, K. 1980. Post-harvest paddy processing and rural women of Bangladesh. Agric. Dev. Agencies News 7(11):8-10.

Sattar, E. 1975. Village women's work. In Women for women, ed. Women for women, Dacca.

Von Harder, G. M. 1975. Women's role in rice processing. In Women for women, ed. Women for women, Dacca.

Wimberly, J. 1974. Observations on the paddy-rice industry in certain TCCA's in Bangladesh. The Ford Foundation, Dacca.

CONSEQUENCES OF SMALL RICE FARM MECHANIZATION IN THE PHILIPPINES: A SUMMARY OF PRELIMINARY ANALYSES

A. M. Aguilar, E. C. Camacho, A. C. Generalla,
P. B. Moran, J. F. Sison, Y. Tan, and J. A. Wicks

A census of eight villages in Cabanatuan City and Guimba, Nueva Ecija, was conducted to provide background information and facilitate the sampling of households for a detailed survey of about 350 landless laborer and farm households and daily record keeping of 50 households. The results of preliminary analyses indicated that mechanization is closely associated with irrigation, but does not directly result in increased yields or cropping intensity. Labor use per hectare was less on mechanized than nonmechanized farms and the reduction was generally due to the lower use of family labor.

Technical, economic, and socioanthropological studies of the output, employment, and income distribution aspects of agricultural mechanization in developing countries have typically attempted to evaluate the problem from within their own narrowly defined concepts of "good vs. bad." It is not surprising that a vast and controversial literature has developed.

The current project was conceived as an attempt to systematized the study of the consequences of mechanization in Southeast Asia. Field sites were located in the Philippines, Thailand, and Indonesia. Preliminary results for the Philippines are presented in this chapter and those for Indonesia in the next two chapters. There were insufficient results available from Thailand.

In the Philippines, the consequences project was conducted in Cabanatuan City and the town of Guimba in Nueva Ecija Province. Four villages representing different levels of mechanization and irrigation were selected from each area. A complete census was carried out in each village and the households were stratified according to occupation, level of mechanization for primary tillage, and irrigation level. About 300 farm and 50 landless households were selected by stratified random sampling for intensive survey. About 50 households from the survey sample were

---

The International Rice Research Institute.

selected for daily record keeping. These record-keeping households were selected from two villages in each area.

This paper summarizes the analyses of the household census data and information collected for the 1979-80 cropping year. The farm and site description is a summary from Moran and Camacho (1981). This is followed by a section on the effects of mechanization on intensity of land use (Generalla and Aguilar 1981), on labor utilization and employment (Sison and Moran 1981), and on production (Tan and Wicks 1981). The chapter ends with brief review of findings to date.

SITE DESCRIPTION

The distribution of household heads by occupation is in Table 1. The proportion of landless laborers is similar in all villages. However, a major difference clearly exists between the two areas in that the villages in Cabanatuan City have a lower proportion of farm operators and a higher proportion of nonagricultural workers than the villages in Guimba.

Some characteristics of the sample villages are in Tables 2-5. Demographically, household characteristics were similar across villages (Table 2), although marked differences were observed in the degree of mechanization (measured in terms of area plowed by machine) and current asset values. Mechanization appeared to be closely associated with irrigation, as evidenced by the farms in the gravity-irrigated villages of San Isidro, Lagare, and Caalibangbangan as compared to those in the rainfed villages (Tables 3 and 4).

Average farm size was similar in all villages except Kalikid Sur, an outlying village characterized by rainfed rice production (Table 6). Rice yield and rice cropping intensity were highest in the irrigated villages and lowest in the rainfed villages.

The pattern of employment and income per household are in Table 7. Results suggest no clear pattern for type of village in which off-farm employment is more important.

Table 1. Distribution of households by occupational group in selected villages.

Village	Total (no.)	Distribution (%) by occupational group		
		Farm operator	Landless laborer	Non-agricultural worker
Cabanatuan City				
San Isidro	200	56	15	29
Lagare	153	70	18	12
Kalikid Sur	282	49	5	46
Caalibangbangan	410	48	17	35
Guimba, Nueva Ecija				
Galvan	134	81	14	5
Narvacan I	89	81	8	11
San Andres	125	87	11	2
Bunol	283	70	17	12
Total	1,676	62	14	24

Table 2. Demographic characteristics by selected villages, 1979 wet season.

Demographic characteristic	Cabanatuan City				Galvan	Guimba, Nueva Ecija		
	San Isidro	Lagare	Kalikid Sur	Caalibang-bangan		Narvacan I	San Andres	Bunol
Households (no.)	49	47	24	77	35	39	45	53
Av age of household head (yr)	48	46	45	45	46	40	42	45
Av education of household head (yr)	4.9	3.7	3.9	4.6	3.9	4.8	5.4	5.1
Av experience in farming (farm operators only) (yr)	22	17	19	21	21	14	17	19
Av household composition								
Male (10 yr and over)	2.4	2.0	2.7	2.3	2.2	2.0	2.2	2.2
Female (10 yr and over)	2.1	2.2	2.0	1.9	2.1	1.6	1.9	2.1
Child (male or female below 10 yr)	1.3	1.2	1.2	1.7	1.2	2.0	1.5	1.2
Total	5.9	5.4	5.9	5.9	5.5	5.6	5.6	5.5
Av no. of permanent laborers/household	0.1	—	—	0.2	0.3	0.3	0.1	0.1

Table 3. Distribution of farm area by level of irrigation in selected villages, 1978 wet season.

Location, village	Total area (ha)	Area rainfed (%)	Area irrigated (%)		
			1 crop	2 crops	3 or more crops
Cabanatuan City					
San Isidro	261	2	16	65	17
Lagare	194	1	20	79	–
Kalikid Sur	374	92	1	7	–
Caalibangbangan	359	1	20	80	–
Guimba, Nueva Ecija					
Galvan	188	91	4	5	–
Narvacan I	130	32	14	54	–
San Andres	216	91	1	7	–
Bunol	422	54	11	35	–

EFFECTS OF MECHANIZATION

Intensity of land use

Data from 42 of the farm record-keeping cooperators were used to examine the impact of mechanization on cropping pattern and intensity. For this analysis, a mechanized farm was defined as one where a two-wheel or four-wheel tractor was used for primary tillage; a nonmechanized farm was one first tilled by draft animals.

Cropping intensity was highest in Lagare and Caalibangbangan (Table 8) where the availability of an adequate gravity irrigation system supports production of two rice crops per year. Although technically feasible, a third crop is seldom grown to maintain soil fertility and to avoid crop pests which would concentrate on a limited area of third crops. Capital available for the third crop also was insufficient. When the data for each irrigation type were segregated by mechanization level, there was insufficient evidence to support the hypothesis of increased cropping intensity on mechanized farms. It appeared likely that irrigation type was the major reason for increased cropping intensity.

Cropping pattern did not differ significantly with method of primary tillage. For both mechanized and nonmechanized farms, rice - rice was dominant on the irrigated farms. Adoption of other patterns, such as vegetable - vegetable and rice -vegetable, depended on management ability and knowledge of potential markets.

The effect of mechanization on turnaround time (the time from harvest of one crop to planting of the next), was studied using a subsample of 29 gravity-irrigated and 9 pump-irrigated parcels. The cropping pattern for all parcels was rice - rice. Turnaround time for the gravity-irrigated parcels was shorter on mechanized than on nonmechanized farms (Table 9). For the pump-irrigated parcels, observations in the mechanized category were insufficient for any meaningful conclusion.

Employment and labor use

Data from the farm survey were used to determine the effects of mechanization on employment and labor use. Farms were classified according to the type of power used for land preparation and threshing. Farms using carabaos for tillage and

Table 4. Distribution of power type for plowing in selected villages, 1978 wet season.

Location, village	Total area (ha)	Distribution (%) of type of plowing					
		Carabao	Two-wheel	Four-wheel	Carabao + 2-wheel	Carabao + 4-wheel	2-wheel + 4-wheel
Cabanatuan City							
San Isidro	261	2	50	1	45	1	–
Lagare	194	6	51	5	27	8	2
Kalikid Sur	374	74	2	8	15	2	1
Caalibangbangan	259	6	18	15	33	14	14
Guimba, Nueva Ecija							
Galvan	188	71	1	2	21	3	2
Narvacan I	130	67	5	15	3	6	4
San Andres	216	29	12	9	29	14	8
Bunol	422	38	2	17	9	7	27

Table 5. Average present value of assets by selected villages, 1979 wet season.[a]

Type of asset	Value ($) of assets							
	Cabanatuan City				Guimba, Nueva Ecija			
	San Isidro (49)	Lagare (47)	Kalikid Sur (24)	Caalibang-bangan (77)	Galvan (35)	Narvacan I (39)	San Andres (45)	Bunol (53)
Draft animals	91	107	336	183	138	234	243	173
Productive animals	92	76	124	45	71	81	79	103
Buildings	122	140	55	132	33	62	148	63
Farm implements or tools	141	139	67	96	53	67	56	58
Agricultural land	1,086	397	727	1,180	1,411	994	2,041	475
Nonagricultural land	582	336	722	368	101	5	57	589
Vehicles	194	115	10	209	–	13	128	15
Home consumer durables	308	155	31	183	86	78	42	78
Farm machinery	378	557	–	312	62	168	326	104
Total value	2,993	2,022	2,074	2,672	1,961	1,703	2,924	1,680

[a]Figures in parentheses indicate number of households.

Table 6. Average farm area, and area and yield of improved rice by selected villages, 1979-80.

Village	Av farm area (ha)	Wet season		Dry season	
		Rice area (ha)	Yield (t/ha)	Rice area (ha)	Yield (t/ha)
Cabanatuan City					
San Isidro	2.35	105	3.2	99	3.6
Lagare	1.82	90	4.5	94	4.7
Kalikid Sur	2.71	40	1.6	–	–
Caalibangbangan	1.81	105	3.7	105	4.3
Guimba, Nueva Ecija					
Galvan	1.74	60	2.0	3	2.9
Narvacan I	1.81	70	2.3	11	2.6
San Andres	1.98	84	1.9	10	1.9
Bunol	2.12	75	2.3	24	3.9

Table 7. Average off-farm employment and income of farmer and landless laborer households by selected villages, 1979-80.

Village	Wet season		Dry season	
	Employment (d/household)	Income ($/household)	Employment (d/household)	Income ($/household)
Cabanatuan City				
San Isidro	50	114	67	132
Lagare	33	53	42	63
Kalikid Sur	50	65	39	117
Caalibangbangan	69	123	43	102
Guimba, Nueva Ecija				
Galvan	59	93	84	159
Narvacan I	7	5	27	62
San Andres	51	71	33	68
Bunol	84	183	68	132

manual labor for threshing were considered nonmechanized. All other farms were defined as mechanized. The mechanized category included the following combinations for land preparation/threshing: carabao/thresher (CT), two-wheel tractor/ manual (TW), two-wheel tractor/thresher (TWT), two-wheel tractor + carabao/ manual (TWC), and two-wheel tractor + carabao-thresher (TWCT).

Labor use, in the wet and dry seasons for each combination is in Table 10. In general, the labor required for a farm operation was reduced significantly whenever mechanical power was used. However, the difference in total labor use between mechanized and nonmechanized farms was not statistically significant. The only significant difference was in labor used for land preparation.

Pooling the data for the wet and dry seasons, use of family labor by mechanized farms was found to be significantly less for all operations than that by nonmechanized farms (Table 11). For hired labor, the difference between farm types was significant only for land preparation.

Table 8. Cropping intensities by village and by farm type, 1979-80.

	Av farm size[a] (ha)	Av effective crop area (ha)		Cropping intensity
		Wet	Dry	
By village				
Cabanatuan City				
Lagare	2.22 (10)	2.22	2.22	2.00
Caalibangbangan	1.74 (12)	1.70	1.70	1.97
Guimba, Nueva Ecija				
San Andres	2.58 (14)	2.29	0.44	1.08
Bunol	2.47 (6)	2.20	0.75	1.25
By farm type				
Gravity irrigated				
Mechanized	1.99 (12)	1.95	1.98	1.98
Nonmechanized	1.79 (7)	1.76	1.75	1.99
Mechanized (wet) and nonmechanized (dry)	2.00 (2)	2.00	2.00	2.00
Nonmechanized (wet) and mechanized (dry)	1.72 (1)	1.72	1.72	1.72
Rainfed and pump				
Mechanized	–	–	–	–
Nonmechanized	3.10 (5)	2.69	0.62	1.20
Pump and pump				
Mechanized	–	–	–	–
Nonmechanized	2.66 (5)	1.89	1.05	1.25
Pump				
Mechanized	–	–	–	–
Nonmechanized	2.60 (3)	2.13	–	1.00
Rainfed				
Mechanized	1.51 (2)	1.51	–	1.00
Nonmechanized	2.00 (3)	1.77	–	0.89
Rainfed mechanized and pump nonmechanized	3.35 (2)	3.35	1.03	1.44

[a]Values in parentheses are the numbers reporting.

Table 9. Turnaround time by mechanization level and irrigation type, 1979-80.

Irrigation type	Turnaround time[a] (d)	
	Mechanized	Nonmechanized
Gravity-irrigated	71.6 (19)	78.0 (10)
Pump-irrigated	20.0 (1)	60.7 (3)
All	69.0 (20)	74.0 (13)

[a]Values in parentheses are the numbers reporting.

Covariance analysis was used to analyze the factors influencing labor use. The model used was:

$$L_i = \alpha_0 + \sum_{j=1}^{4} \alpha_j M_j + \alpha_5 S + \alpha_6 I + \alpha_7 T \, \alpha_8 A + \sum_{j=9}^{12} \alpha_j IM_j + \alpha_{13} SA + e$$

Table 10. Labor use for various farm operations, crop year 1979-80.

Farm classification	Land preparation		Planting		Care or cultivation		Postproduction		Total (h)
	h	%	h	%	h	%	h	%	
			Wet season						
Carabao	105	18	198	33	34	6	251	43	588
Carabao/thresher	112	19	211	35	32	5	242	41	597
Two-wheel	30	6	211	43	22	4	233	47	496
Two-wheel/thresher	37	8	199	45	26	6	182	41	444
Two-wheel/carabao	61	12	178	36	32	6	224	46	495
Two-wheel/carabao/thresher	54	11	208	42	24	5	206	42	492
			Dry season						
Carabao	143	23	222	35	26	4	235	38	626
Carabao/thresher	158	20	291	37	32	4	314	39	795
Two-wheel	59	9	217	33	36	6	340	52	652
Two-wheel/thresher	33	8	190	44	29	6	182	42	434
Two-wheel/carabao	58	11	228	43	29	5	216	41	531
Two-wheel/carabao/thresher	55	13	166	38	32	7	181	42	434

Table 11. Comparison of use of family and hired labor for various activities by land preparation, crop year 1979-80.[a]

Operation	Family labor (h)			Hired labor (h)		
	Non-mechanized preparation	Mechanized land preparation	Difference	Non-mechanized preparation	Mechanized land preparation	Difference
Land preparation	99	35	64***	24	10	14***
Planting	41	17	24***	187	177	10
Care and cultivation	31	25	6*	2	3	-1
Postproduction	75	19	56***	187	186	1
Total	246	96	150*	400	376	24

[a]Significant at the 1% (***) and 10% (*) levels.

where L_i is the number of man-hours of 1) total labor, 2) total hired labor, and 3) total family labor;

M_1 is a mechanization dummy taking the value of one (1) if the farm uses the TW combination and zero (0) otherwise;

M_2 is a mechanization dummy taking the value of one for TWC and zero otherwise;

M_3 is mechanization dummy taking the value of one for TWT and zero otherwise; and

M_4 is one for TWCT and zero otherwise.

S is a season dummy which takes the value of one for the dry season and zero for the wet season;

I is an irrigation dummy which takes the value of one for irrigated farms and zero for rainfed farms;

T is a tenure status dummy which takes the value of one for owner-occupied farms and zero otherwise;

A is the total land area, in hectares, devoted to rice;

e is the residual term.

All mechanization dummies are zero for the C and CT combinations. The coefficients of the mechanization dummies were interpreted as measures of group differences between mechanized and nonmechanized farms.

To test the significance of the interaction effects of irrigation and mechanization, as well as season and area, the following relationship, without interactions, was estimated:

$$L_i = \alpha_o + \sum_{j=1}^{4} \alpha_j M_j + \alpha_5 S + \alpha_6 I + \alpha_7 T + \alpha_8 A + e^*$$

Application of the F test revealed no significant difference in the explanatory power of the model following inclusion of the interaction terms. The results in Table 12 and the subsequent discussion are restricted to the model without interactions.

In all equations, area had a significant positive effect on labor use. All types of mechanization had a significant negative impact on the use of family labor and the TWT and TWCT combinations had a negative significant impact on total labor use. With the exception of TW for total hired labor, all other machine use variables were negative but not significant. It appears that only use of family labor is affected by mechanization. Finally, tenure status had no impact on labor use.

Production

The effects of mechanization on production were evaluated using a subsample of the survey data. The subsample comprised those farms using carabao only for land preparation and those using the two-wheel tractor only for land preparation. Average input/output coefficients for the two groups of farms are in Table 13.

The analytical method used was decomposition analysis, a mathematical procedure for partitioning an aggregate into component elements or explanatory factors. The procedure outlined by Binswanger (1978 and 1979) was modified to permit evaluating the impact of changes in yield, area, cropping intensity, and price.

Table 12. Estimated difference in labor use in rice production among farms with different modes of mechanization, crop year 1979-80.[a]

Independent variable	Total hired labor	Total family labor	Total labor
Intercept	−37.01	223.55**	182.65**
	(−0.63)	(7.82)	(3.18)
Two-wheel (M_1)	−146.97	−182.51**	−37.61
	(−1.77)	(−4.52)	(−0.46)
Two-wheel/carabao (M_2)	58.89	−147.50**	−89.59
	(0.79)	(−4.04)	(−1.22)
Two-wheel/thresher (M_3)	−47.19	−134.83**	−185.13**
	(0.80)	(−4.68)	(−3.20)
Two-wheel + carabao/thresher (M_4)	−8.04	−155.32**	−164.96**
	(−0.12)	(−4.85)	(−2.56)
Seasonal effect (S)	17.55	−47.96***	−28.89
	(0.39)	(−2.19)	(−0.66)
Irrigation (I)	55.88	−55.62***	0.19
	(1.22)	(−2.48)	(0.004)
Tenure (T)	−1.85	−1.68	−4.10
	(−0.04)	(−0.08)	(−0.10)
Area (A)	368.27**	72.55**	443.45**
	(18.22)	(7.36)	(22.41)

[a]Values in parentheses are calculated t-values. Values outside the parentheses are significant at the 1% (***) and 5% (**) levels.

Table 13. Characteristics of sample farms by type of mechanization, 1979 wet season.

Operation	Carabao farms	Two-wheel tractor farms
Farms (no.)	46	62
Area (ha)	1.95	2.39
Production (kg)	5090	7711
Yield (kg/ha)	2610	4013
Price of paddy ($/kg)	0.14	0.16
Total preharvest labor (h/ha)	247	223
Total postproduction labor (h/ha)	244	207
Total land preparation hours (h/ha)	97	30
Level of fertilizer (kg N/ha)	40	58
Value of crop protection ($/ha)	13	25
Loan for seasonal farm expense ($/ha)	139	165
Long-term loan for agricultural investment ($/ha)	266	338

Two approaches were used for the analysis. The first was an arithmetic decomposition model based on the formulations of Krishna (1974) and Binswanger (1978) and derived from the output identity:

$$Q = C \sum_i A_i P_i X_i$$

where Q is the value of total output;

C is the cropping intensity defined as the gross cropped area divided by the operated area;

A_i is the weighted proportion of gross cropped area under crop i;

X_i is the yield of crop i (kg/ha); and

P_i is the price of crop i ($/kg).

Having recognized the possibility of obtaining different solutions from the same data set, the formula was revised for consistency (Tan et al 1981). This required several interaction terms.

A second decomposition model was used to investigate the yield effect. It was a modification of Bisaliah (1977) and was derived from the Cobb-Douglas production function:

$$Y = \beta_o e^{\alpha_o D} F^{(\beta_1 + \alpha_1 D)} L^{(\beta_2 + \alpha_2 D)} C^{(\beta_3 + \alpha_3 D)} P^{(\beta_4 + \alpha_4 D)} e^U$$

where Y is the yield of paddy (kg/ha);

L is the preharvest labor used in planting, care and cultivation of the crop, except land preparation (man-hours/ha);

F is the total amount of fertilizer used (kg N/ha);

C is the total amount of crop protection chemicals used ($/ha);

P is the total amount of machine and animal services used in land preparation (h/ha);

D is a dummy equal to 1 for mechanized farms and 0 for nonmechanized farms;

β_o is the scale parameter;

$\beta_1 - \beta_4$ are the output elasticities;

α_o is the intercept shifter;

$\alpha_1 - \alpha_4$ are the slope shifters;

e^U is the error term with e defined as the mathematical constant and U normally distributed.

Results for the decomposition of output into yield, area, cropping intensity, and price are in Table 14. Yield had the greatest effect on output, followed by cropping intensity. The area and price effects were relatively small. The only interaction term of any importance was between cropping intensity and yield.

The possible impact of mechanization on yield was further investigated using the second decomposition model. The results (Table 15) were consistent with respect to the expected signs of coefficients, although not all variables turned out to be significant. For mechanized farms, the significant variables were fertilizer use and power; for nonmechanized farms, only crop protection was significant.

By decomposing the total yield differences into the effects of technical change and changes in inputs, technical change was found to increase yield by 49% (Table 16). The technical change was further disaggregated into a nonneutral component, accounting for 58% of the change, and a neutral component accounting for −9%. This implied that production on mechanized farms was higher than on nonmechanized farms because of different responses to the inputs used. Total change in yield

Table 14. Decomposition analysis (with interaction terms) of output differences between two-wheel tractor and carabao farms.

Sources of output differences	Absolute change (kg)	Percentage share
Individual effects		
Pure yield effect	4357	31
Area effect	1557	11
Cropping intensity effect	3609	26
Price effect	689	5
First-order interaction effects		
Yield and price	397	3
Area and price	−72	−1
Area and yield	389	3
Cropping intensity and yield	1794	13
Cropping intensity and price	284	2
Cropping intensity and area	641	5
Second-order interaction effects		
Cropping intensity, price and area	−29	−
Cropping intensity, price and yield	164	1
Cropping intensity, yield and area	160	1
Price, yield and area	−47	−
Third-order interaction effect		
Cropping intensity, price, yield and area	−19	−
Total	13873	−

Table 15. Estimated coefficients of the Cobb-Douglas production functions for two-wheel tractor and carabao farms.[a]

Independent variable	Coefficients[b]	
	Carabao farms	Two-wheel tractor farms
Intercept	5.7***	5.14***
Power	0.02	0.20**
Fertilizer use (kg N/ha)	0.034	0.44***
Labor (h/ha)	0.005	0.10
Crop protection ($/ha)	0.34***	0.01
R^2	0.33	0.65
N	46	62

[a]Dependent variable − yield per hectare. [b]Significant at 1% (***) and 5% (**) levels.

due to differences in the levels of inputs was estimated at 4%, the highest contributor being fertilizer followed by capital services.

The extent to which these nonneutral technological changes, relating predominantly to the efficiency of fertilizer and crop protection chemical, can be attributed to mechanization is unclear. The possibility of other underlying variables explaining these differences needs to be carefully examined before making any firm conclusions.

Table 16. Decomposition analysis of per hectare yield differences between two-wheel tractor and carabao farms.

Sources of yield differences	Percentage share
Technical change	
Neutral technical change	−9
Nonneutral technical change	58
Total due to technical change	49
Change in inputs	
Power	−3
Fertilizer	7
Labor	−0
Crop protection	0
Total due to input difference	4
Total due to all sources	53

Finally, cropping intensity, the second major component explaining differences in output, was examined using a covariance model. Results indicated that irrigation type, rather than availability of tillage machinery, was the major determinant of cropping intensity.

CONCLUSIONS

A few preliminary conclusions can be made. First, although many of the characteristics of the eight villages were similar, they had very different levels of irrigation and mechanization. Mechanized farms usually produced more, had higher yields and cropping intensity and used less labor per hectare, particularly family labor. However, the evidence suggested that except for labor use, these differences were more likely to be associated with irrigation than with mechanization. Further detailed analysis is required to verify these preliminary conclusions.

REFERENCES CITED

Binswanger, H. P. 1978. The economics of tractors in South Asia. Agricultural Development Council, New York, and International Crops Research Institute for the Semi-Arid Tropics, Hyderabad, India.

Binswanger, H. P. 1979. A note on decomposition without residual. Consequences of small rice farm mechanization workshop, October 1-4, Los Baños, Laguna.

Bisaliah, S. 1977. Decomposition analysis of output change under new production technology in wheat farming: some implication to return to investment in research. Indian J. Agric. Econ. 32(3):193-201.

Generalla, A., and A. Aguilar. 1981. Effects of mechanization on intensity of land use. Consequences of Small Rice Farm Mechanization Project Working Pap. 35. Los Baños, Laguna.

Khrishna, R. 1974. Measurement of the direct and indirect employment effects of agricultural growth in technological change. E. O. Edwards, ed. Employment in developing nations. Columbia University Press.

Moran, P., and E. C. Camacho. 1981. Consequences of farm mechanization project site description: Philippines. Consequences of Small Rice Farm Mechanization Project Working Pap. 34. Los Baños, Laguna.

Sison, J. F., and P. B. Moran. 1981. Farm labor utilization and employment in two selected municipalities in Nueva Ecija — a preliminary analysis. Consequences of Small Rice Farm Mechanization Project Working Pap. 37. Los Baños, Laguna.

Tan, Y. L., J. P. Webster, and J. A. Wicks. 1981. The decomposition of differences in output between two groups of farms. Consequences of Small Rice Farm Mechanization Project Working Pap. 14. Los Baños, Laguna.

Tan, Y. L., and J. A. Wicks. 1981. Production effects of mechanization. Consequences of Small Rice Farm Mechanization Project Working Pap. 36. Los Baños, Laguna.

CONSEQUENCES OF SMALL RICE FARM MECHANIZATION IN WEST JAVA: A SUMMARY OF PRELIMINARY ANALYSES

Y. Saefudin, H. Siswosumarto, R. Bernsten, A. Sri Bagyo,
J. Lingard, and J. Wicks

A census was conducted of 200 households in each of 8 villages in Subang and Indramayu districts, West Java. A stratified random sample of 360 households was selected for intensive survey and a subsample of 48 households selected for daily record keeping. Preliminary results from the study suggested that mechanization has no impact on yields and very little impact, if any, on cropping intensity. Mechanization also resulted in a considerable decline in labor use. More detailed analysis is required before firm conclusions can be reached.

Agricultural extension agents and government officials have claimed there is a power shortage for land preparation in Java. They suggest, this causes overdependence on draft animal and manual methods, resulting in delays and reduced cropping intensity. They also contend that, because power tillers and tractors can prepare the land deeper and more thoroughly, mechanized land preparation will lead to increased yields. Such arguments have been used to encourage farmers to purchase power tillers in the densely populated islands of Java and Bali and minitractors in the sparsely inhabited outer islands of Sulawesi and Sumatra.

The West Java component of the Consequences of Small Rice Farm Mechanization Project was implemented as a cooperative research project between the Rural Dynamics Study/Agro-Economic Survey (RDS/SAE) group and the International Rice Research Institute (IRRI). Data were collected in 1979 and 1980, and covered two dry seasons and one wet season. Results are summarized from Saefuddin (1981), Siswosumarto (1981), Sinaga (1981), and Bagyo and Lingard (1981).

Agro-Economic Survey; Sub-Directorate of Agricultural Mechanization, Indonesia; IRRI/Central Research Institute for Agriculture Cooperative Program, Bogor, Indonesia; Central Research Institute for Agriculture; IRRI; and IRRI.

SITE DESCRIPTION

West Java, one of the 27 provinces of Indonesia, is known as the rice granary of the country. It is also the area where most of the tractors are located. The province covers 46,300 km² and, in 1978, had a population of 24.7 million. Fifty-two percent of the population was classified as adult and 70% worked in agriculture. Of the 63% of the land which was farmed, 1.85 million ha were lowland, of which 72% was irrigated. Of the irrigated area 82% was double-cropped with rice. The average yield of rice is more than 3 t/ha and tends to be around 5% higher than the national average. From 1974 to 1978, the number of tractors in the province increased by 168% from 431 to 1,154.

The research sites were selected through a combination of random and purposeful procedures. The distribution of tractors in the province was determined through reference to secondary data on farm area, production, and number of tractors in the 20 districts. Subang and Indramayu districts were selected because of the importance of rice production and the number of tractors. The districts are on the north coastal plain of Java, some 160-200 km east of Jakarta and 60 km north of the provincial capital of Bandung.

The eight subdistricts — four from each district —with the greatest number of tractors were selected. Then four villages with four or more tractors were randomly selected from each subdistrict and a block census, covering 200 households/village, was undertaken. A stratified random sample of 300 farm and 60 landless laborer households was drawn from the census population and a subsample of 60 households obtained from that sample. These were used for the survey and daily record-keeping activities, respectively.

Some characteristics of the villages are in Table 1. Except for Gabuskulon, all the villages were almost completely irrigated. Compared to those in the Philippines, the villages were extremely large and the number of two-wheel tractors per village ranged from 4 in Bojongtengah to 76 in Anjatan.

Some characteristics of the survey respondents by mechanization level are in Table 2. Except for more formal education and the increased employment of permanent laborers, the mechanized households were very similar to the non-mechanized households.

EFFECTS OF MECHANIZATION

Intensity of land use

Survey data for the 1979 dry season and 1979-80 wet season were used to evaluate the effect of mechanization on cropping intensity and timeliness. Farms were categorized according to the method of initial land preparation.

It is argued that if a labor shortage is responsible for delays in land preparation, farmers owning or using power tillers should be able to prepare land more rapidly. However, mechanized farms in the study had only slightly higher cropping intensities (Table 3). Also remember that the planting of a third crop in the survey area had been encouraged by the first year of the government's INPRES (President's Interaction) program to stimulate secondary crop production. Because tiller owners tended

Table 1. Characteristics of sample villages, 1979.

Sample villages	Population	Households			Farmland			Hand tractors (no.)
		Total (no.)	Farmer (%)	Landless (%)	Total (no.)	Lowland (%)	Irrigated (%)	
Indramayu								
Sukadana	4,057	912	88[a]		459	416	99	11
Gabuskulon	12,687	2,841	90[a]		2,911	2,476	67	16
Anjatan	28,788	6,346	46	43	4,054	3,631	100	76
Sukra	13,081	4,785		80	1,664	1,474	100	19
Subang								
Bojongtengah	5,622	1,560	87[a]		954	896	100	4
Pamanukan hilir	8,450	1,950	47	40	566	505	100	21
Mariuk	7,293	2,045	47	48	1,194	1,116	100	44
Tambakdahan	10,279	2,555	31	67	NA	1,139	100	5

[a]Total of farmer and landless households. Source: Sample Village Offices, 1979.

Table 2. Characteristics of survey respondents, 1979-80.

Characteristics	1979-80 wet season				1980 dry season		
	Nonmechanized		Mechanized[a]		Nonmechanized	Mechanized[a]	
	Manual	Animal	Hire	Owner	Manual	Hire	Owner
No. reporting	56	100	61	68	161	61	64
Head of household							
Age (yr)	39	39.3	39.6	40	39.4	39.7	40
Education (yr)	2.6	3.6	5.1	5	3.3	5	4.9
Farming experience (yr)	13.6	15.2	15.2	15.2	14.6	14.9	14.7
Household members (no.)	4.6	4.8	4.7	4.7	4.5	5.1	4.5
Males (no.)	1.7	1.6	1.7	1.8	1.7	1.7	1.7
Females (no.)	1.5	1.4	1.7	1.5	1.5	1.7	1.4
Children (no.)	1.4	1.8	1.3	1.4	1.3	1.7	1.4
Permanent laborers (no.)	0.1	0.2	0.1	0.8	0.1	0.2	0.8

[a]Two-wheel tractor.

Table 3. Sample characteristics, cropping pattern, and cropping intensity, by power source, 1978-79.[a]

	Manual	Animal		Tractor		
	WS and DS	WS only	WS and DS	WS only	DS only	WS and DS
Sample size	58	112	2	47	8	73
Total area (ha)	64.7	185.6	5.8	123.5	15.6	297.7
Cropping pattern (%)						
Rice - rice	93.0	85.7	100	80.9	62.5	86.3
Rice - rice - secondary	7	14.3	0	19.1	37.5	13.7
Cropping intensity	2.07	2.14	2	2.19	2.38	2.14
		2.14			2.17	

[a]WS is wet season, DS is dry season.

to be larger land owners and community leaders, it is likely that they were more responsive to government demonstration programs.

The time taken to complete land preparation after water became available was investigated for each category. During the wet season, farmers using manual land preparation completed the operation first, followed by animal users, tractor owners, and tractor renters. During the dry season, tractor owners and renters completed land preparation first, and farmers using manual land preparation were last. Land preparation was started 7-14 days later on manual farms. The most likely reasons for these differences relate to farm size and labor availability. The nonmechanized farms tend to be much smaller than the mechanized ones and farmers using manual land preparation usually hire sufficient labor to do the job rapidly. In the wet season, it would be reasonable to expect nonmechanized farms to complete land preparation earlier. At the beginning of the dry season, most labor is busy with harvesting, which pays substantially more than land preparation. This is likely to delay land preparation.

To verify the impact of mechanization on cropping intensity and timeliness, farmers' reasons for using a tractor were examined. None of the 68 tractor owners indicated interest in growing a third crop as a reason for purchasing a tractor. The most important reasons were to reduce costs of land preparation (51%), plant the crop on time (24%), and plow deeper or more thoroughly (22%). Of the 263 farmers questioned why they did not grow a third crop, 39% reported risk — particularly from rat damage, 20% had no time after the second rice crop, 16% had poor drainage, 15% said it is not a common practice in the area, and 9% claimed a water shortage. It appears that the potential for increasing cropping intensity will be achieved only if all farmers can be strongly motivated to work together and if seed, fertilizer, pesticides, water, and credit can be made available when needed.

Labor use

A detailed classification of the mechanization level was developed to examine the impact of mechanization on labor use. Those who gave incomplete information were excluded and data from the remaining 282 respondents were used in the analysis. The respondents were classified as fully mechanized (T_1) if they used tractors only, fully manual (M_1) if they used manual labor only, animal-manual (A_1)

Table 4. Tests for differences in labor use and farm size[a] between mechanized and non-mechanized farms, 1979-80 wet season.

Comparison[b]	Labor use (man-days/ha)			Annual labor use (man-days/farm)	Farm size (ha)
	Wet season	Dry season	Annual		
T_1 vs M_1	−57**	−37**	−106**	396**	3.61**
T_1 vs A_1	−34**	−27**	− 62**	301**	3.01*
T_1 vs M_2	−35**	−21**	− 42**	324**	3.15**
T_2 vs M_1	−49**	−28**	− 84**	426**	3.09**
T_2 vs A_1	−26**	−18*	− 40*	331**	2.49**
T_2 vs M_2	−27**	−12	− 23	354**	2.59**

[a]Significant at the 5% (*) and 1% levels (**). [b]T_1 = fully mechanized, T_2 = mainly mechanized, M_1 = fully manual, M_2 = mainly manual, A_1 = animal-manual.

Table 5. Decomposition analysis of labor use differences between mechanized and nonmechanized farms.

Sources of differences	Percentage share[a]					
	T_1 vs M_1	T_1 vs A_1	T_1 vs M_2	T_2 vs M_1	T_2 vs A_1	T_2 vs M_2
Individual effects						
Labor use per ha effect	-21	-29	-26	-14	-17	-15
Area effect	207	202	201	165	152	153
Cropping intensity effect	-6	-10	-10	-3	-5	-5
First-order interaction effects						
Labor use per ha and area	-69	-53	-53	-41	-25	-26
Labor use per ha and cropping intensity	2	3	3	1	1	1
Area and cropping intensity	-20	-18	-21	-9	-7	-9
Second-order interaction effect						
Labor use per ha, area and cropping intensity	7	5	5	2	1	2

[a]T_1 = fully mechanized, T_2 = mainly mechanized, M_1 = fully manual, M_2 = mainly manual, A_1 = animal-manual.

if 50% animal and 50% manual, mainly mechanized (T_2) if 75% of the land preparation was done by tractor, mainly manual (M_2) if 75% of the land preparation was done manually, and mixed (T_3) if they used tractor, animal, and manual in a combination which could not otherwise be classified.

A t-test was used to determine the significance of differences in labor use and total labor use per farm between mechanized and nonmechanized farms. The results in Table 4 indicate that labor use per hectare is less on mechanized than on nonmechanized farms. In only two cases was the difference not significant at the 5% level. In all cases, labor use per farm was significantly higher on mechanized than nonmechanized farms, mainly because of the size difference.

A decomposition analysis, using the procedure of Tan (1981), confirmed that farm size was the only factor having a major positive effect on labor use by mechanized compared to nonmechanized farms (Table 5). Smaller, but negative, effects were found for labor use per hectare and cropping intensity effects.

Yield

Data on yield, fertilizer use, and crop failure for the 1979 dry season, 1979-80 wet season, and 1980 dry season by mechanization level are in Table 6. In all cases, the

Table 6. Yield, fertilizer use, and crop failure.

	Nonmechanized			Mechanized		
	Manual	Animal	Aggregate	Hire	Owner	Aggregate
1979 dry season						
No. reporting	217	–	217	–	–	81
Fertilizer						
Urea (kg/ha)	213	–	213	–	–	219
Triple superphosphate (kg/ha)	63	–	63	–	–	81
Total (kg/ha)	276	–	276	–	–	300
Yield (kg/planted ha)	2835	–	2835	–	–	2975
1979-80 wet season						
No. reporting	56	100	156	61	68	129
Fertilizer						
Urea (kg/ha)	226	250	241	238	242	240
Triple superphosphate (kg/ha)	74	70	71	81	84	83
Total (kg/ha)	300	320	313	319	326	323
Yield (kg/planted ha)	4613	4966	4839	5116	4709	4901
1980 dry season						
No. reporting	161	–	161	61	64	125
Fertilizer						
Urea (kg/ha)	207	–	207	220	230	225
Triple superphosphate (kg/ha)	72	–	72	84	71	77
Total (kg/ha)	279	–	279	304	301	302
Yield (kg/planted ha)	2993	–	2993	3632	3528	3579
Crop failure (%)	24	–	24	2.6	2.6	2.6
Yield (kg/harvested ha)	3938	–	3938	–	–	3675

yield per planted hectare was greater on mechanized than on nonmechanized farms. However, in the 1980 dry season, there was a considerable amount of crop failure, particularly on the nonmechanized farms, so that the yield per harvested hectare was much higher on nonmechanized than on mechanized farms. During all seasons, the mechanized farms used the same, or slightly more, urea per hectare and considerably more triple superphosphate.

Comparison of the differences in yield per harvested hectare and total fertilizer use reveals the average output per kilogram of fertilizer should have been at least 5.8 kg in the 1979 dry season, 5.6 kg in the 1979-80 wet season, and negative in the 1980 dry season if the difference in fertilizer use alone was to account for the yield difference. Such values appear to be highly plausible.

The farm classification used for analysis of labor use was also used for a more detailed analysis of yields. Results of the t-tests for differererences in yield and total production are in Table 7. Other than for the M_2 category, yield by both season and year was higher on mechanized than on nonmechanized farms. In several instances, however, the difference was not significant at the 5% level. Annual output per farm was significantly higher on mechanized than on nonmechanized farms. That was expected because mechanized farms were also significantly larger than nonmechanized farms (Table 4).

Decomposition analysis was used to determine the extent to which the differences in output could be attributed to differences in farm size rather than to yield or cropping intensity effects. The results in Table 8 indicate the area or farm size effect was the major explanator of differences in output. Yield and the interaction between yield and area had an effect although they were less important.

To investigate whether the yield differences between mechanized and nonmechanized farms could be explained by factors other than mechanization, the levels of input use by different types of farm were compared and a Cobb-Douglas production function for total output was estimated. Table 9 reveals little pattern, or significance, in the differences in input use per hectare between the different farm categories. For the Cobb-Douglas function (Table 10), some 87% of the variation in yield was explained by the independent variables. Farm size, nitrogen use, and insecticides were all significant at the 1% level, and triple superphosphate at the 5% level. The sum of 1.05 for the coefficients suggested constant returns to scale across the sample,

Table 7. Tests for differences in yield and output between mechanized and nonmechanized farms[a].

| Comparison[b] | Yield (kg/ha) | | | Annual production (kg/farm) |
	Wet season	Dry season	Annual	
T_1 vs M_1	411*	647*	1,102**	27,332**
T_1 vs A_1	159	974**	1,225**	22,615**
T_1 vs M_2	−401	196	−155	22,038**
T_2 vs M_1	458*	531	1,096	26,129**
T_2 vs A_1	206	858**	1,219**	21,412**
T_2 vs M_2	−354	80	−161	20,835**

[a] Significant at the 5% (*) and 1% (**) levels. [b] T_1 = fully mechanized, T_2 = mainly mechanized, M_1 = fully manual, M_2 = mainly manual, A_1 = animal-manual.

Table 8. Decomposition analysis of output differences between mechanized and nonmechanized farms.

Source of differences	Percentage share[a]					
	T_1 vs M_1	T_1 vs A_1	T_1 vs M_2	T_2 vs M_1	T_2 vs A_1	T_2 vs M_2
Individual effects						
Yield effect	4	5	-2	5	8	1
Area effect	97	100	123	87	87	10.7
Cropping intensity effect	-3	-5	-6	-2	-3	-4
First-order interaction effect						
Yield and area	13	10	-3	16	12	2
Yield and cropping intensity	—	—	—	—	—	—
Area and cropping intensity	-9	-9	-13	-5	-4	7
Second-order interaction effect						
Yield area and cropping intensity	-1	-1	—	-1	-1	—

[a] T_1 = fully mechanized, M_1 = mainly mechanized, M_2 = mainly manual, A_1 = animal-manual.

Table 9. Tests for differences in input use between mechanized and nonmechanized farms.[a]

Comparison[b]	Nitrogen (kg/ha)			Triple superphosphate (kg/ha)			Pesticides ($/ha)		
	Wet season	Dry season	Annual	Wet season	Dry season	Annual	Wet season	Dry season	Annual
T_1 vs M_1	-1	-1	-6	13	5	19	-0.92	-0.67	-1.48
T_1 vs A_1	23**	7	27**	28**	22**	50**	-4.12**	-3.15**	-6.74**
T_1 vs M_2	-15	-9	-24	-10	1	-1	0.51	-0.68	0.56
T_2 vs M_1	-3	9	6	15	20	33*	-1.28	-0.11	-0.05
T_2 vs A_1	21*	17	39**	30**	37**	64**	-4.57	-2.60	-5.74*
T_2 vs M_2	-17	1	-12	-8	-16	13	0.15	-0.13	1.56

[a] Significant at the 5% (*) and 1% (**) levels. [b] T_1 = fully mechanized, T_2 = mainly manual, M_1 = fully manual, M_2 = mainly manual, A_1 = animal-manual.

Table 10. Cobb-Douglas production function with production (kg/farm) as dependent variable and two dummy variables.

Independent variable	Regression coefficients[a]
Farm size	0.77 (10.36)***
Nitrogen (kg/farm)	0.22 (4.37)***
Triple superphosphate (kg/farm)	0.06 (1.92)*
Insecticide ($/farm)	−0.07 (2.79)**
Labor (man-days/farm)	0.07 (1.10)
Mechanization dummy:	
T_1	0.03 (0.64)
T_2	−0.04 (0.73)
Intercept	6.38
No. of observation	596
R^2	0.87
F value	474.77

[a] Figures in parentheses are t values. Significant at the 5% (*), 1% (**) and 0.5% (***) levels.

but the mechanization dummies for T_1 (purely mechanized farms) and T_2 (mainly mechanized farms) were both small and insignificant. The negative sign for the T_2 coefficient was, however, surprising. An alternative specification, using yield per hectare as the dependent variable, produced no improvement in the results.

CONCLUSIONS

The preliminary evidence from the West Java data suggested that mechanization has very little impact on cropping intensity. Most farmers in the survey site were already double-cropping and a quantum leap, involving a complete package of inputs, credits, and incentives, would be required to have a significant impact on cropping intensity. Similarly, any increased yields on mechanized farms could be explained by higher use of inputs other than machinery. Mechanization was also clearly demonstrated to result in lower levels of labor use.

However, before drawing any policy conclusions from these results, remember that the mechanized farms were larger than the nonmechanized farms even before adopting tractors. Whether the smaller farms, typical of Java, can support mechanized technology, and what the overall effect would be, is not yet clear. These questions require further analysis.

REFERENCES CITED

Bagyo, A. S., and J. Lingard. 1981. The impact of mechanization on production and employment in rice areas of West Java. Consequences of Small Rice Farm Mechanization Project Working Paper 43. Los Baños, Laguna.

Saefuddin, Y. 1981. Site description: West Java. Consequences of Small Rice Farm Mechanization Project Working Paper 38. Los Baños, Laguna.

Sinaga, R. S. 1981. The effect of mechanization on productivity in West Java. Consequences of Small Rice Farm Mechanization Project Working Paper 41. Los Baños, Laguna.

Siswosumarto, H. 1981. Effects of mechanization on intensity of land use, West Java, Indonesia. Consequences of Small Rice Farm Mechanization Project Working Paper 39. Los Baños, Laguna.

Tan, Y. L. 1981. The impact of farm mechanization on small-scale rice production. MS thesis, University of the Philippines at Los Baños, Laguna.

CONSEQUENCES OF SMALL RICE FARM MECHANIZATION IN SOUTH SULAWESI: A SUMMARY OF PRELIMINARY ANALYSES

Y. Maamum, I. G. P. Sarasutha, J. Hafsah, R. Bernsten,
R. Sinaga, and J. Wicks

A census was conducted of about 2,000 households in 8 villages in Pinrang and Sidrap districts, South Sulawesi. Results were used to stratify the population by level of irrigation and mechanization prior to sampling 290 households for survey. A subsample of 70 was then selected for daily record keeping. Initial analyses suggested that mechanization of land preparation had no impact on cropping intensity in irrigated areas but a slight positive impact in rainfed areas. No impact on yield was detected in either environment. Mechanization resulted in a decline in labor use, particularly at land preparation time. Most of the labor saved was family labor.

South Sulawesi was chosen as a research site for the consequences of mechanization study because it is one of the few provinces in the sparsely populated, outer islands of Indonesia where tractors have been used for several years. In contrast to the two-wheel tractors usually encountered in West Java, the most common type in South Sulawesi is the four-wheel minitractor imported from Japan, with a 12- to 15-hp engine.

The project was conducted in South Sulawesi as cooperative research with the Maros Research Institute for Food Crops (LPPM), Provincial Agricultural Extension (DIPERTA), Hasanuddin University (UNHAS), and the International Rice Research Institute (IRRI), with Agro Economic Survey (SAE) as the national coordinator.

Results summarized in this paper are from Maamun (1981), Sarasutha and Bernsten (1981), Bernsten (1981), and Sinaga (1981).

Maros Agricultural Research Institute for Food Crops, Indonesia; Maros Agricultural Research Institute for Food Crops; Dinas Pertanian, Indonesia; IRRI/Central Research Institute for Agriculture Cooperative Program, Bogor, Indonesia; Agro-Economic Survey; and IRRI.

SITE DESCRIPTION

With 63% of the labor force working in agriculture, South Sulawesi has a total of 1,170 villages spread over 72,781 km². Only 12% of the land area is farmed, including 521,919 ha of lowland and 407,222 of upland. The remaining 88% is forest, mountains, rivers, swamps, and homelots (Maamun and Patong 1978). On the 760,993 ha planted to food crops (about 20% of which was double-cropped), wetland rice was grown on 66%, dryland rice on 26%, maize on 22%, cassava on 4.2%, and peanuts and vegetables on 3.2% (SSAC 1976). Rice production in 1976 averaged 330 kg/person (SSAEO 1978), so that with an annual consumption of 120 kg/person South Sulawesi was a major rice surplus area, exporting 1.2 million t.

The two districts for the research were selected through a combination of random and purposeful sampling. Secondary data on farm area, production, and tractor numbers suggested the contiguous districts of Sidrap and Pinrang, with 51% of the tractors in the province, to be the most appropriate. They are located about 200 km north of Ujung Pandang, the provincial capital. Both districts are predominantly agricultural with most males classified as farmers. The remainder are engaged predominantly in nonfarm activities, there being few landless laborers in the area. In 1976, rice output was 783 kg/person in Pinrang and 1,416 kg/person in Sidrap. Mechanized land preparation was first introduced in both districts in 1974, and in 1978 there were 165 minitractors in Sidrap and 138 in Pinrang. The number rose to 300 and 208, respectively, the next year. In addition to these tractors, 16,389 carabaos are used for land preparation in Sidrap and 7,254 in Pinrang.

Secondary data indicated that the tractors in Sidrap and Pinrang were most common in eight of the subdistricts: three in Sidrap and five in Pinrang. Four villages were randomly selected from each of those groups at subdistricts.

The number of households, household size, and number of farm households for each village are in Table 1. A block census, covering the eight villages, of about 2,000 households was conducted. The census facilitated classification of the households by

Table 1. Distribution of households, farm households, and number of household members.[a]

Village	Households (no.)	Persons/ household	Farm households (no.)
Pinrang			
Padakkalawa	967	5.2	928
Mattiro Deceng	1355	5.1	1300
Temmasarange	1503	6.9	1277
Matongang-tongang	1345	5.1	1319
Subtotal	5170	5.6	4824
Sidrap			
Rappang	2036	5.1	479
Watang Sidenreng	1078	6.1	1089
Lancirang	1463	5.9	613
Tanru-Tedong	3086	6.9	2792
Subtotal	7663	6.0	4973
Total	12833	–	9719

[a]Source: Village office, Sidrap and Pinrang, 1979.

irrigation status and mechanization level (man, animal, or combination of man and animal for nonmechanized farms and man-tractor or man-animal-tractor for mechanized). Wherever possible, a random sample of 30 households was drawn from each category. For each category having 30 or fewer observations, the entire category was selected. This provided a final sample of 290 households. A subsample of 70 households was selected for daily record keeping.

The average farm size and distribution of irrigation type by village are shown in Table 2. Some 85% of the rice land was irrigated. The four villages in Pinrang and Waterang Sidenrang in Sidrap were served by water from the Saddang irrigation system, Tanru-Tedong and Lancirang by Bulu Cenrana, and Rappang by Bulo. The semitechnical and simple irrigation systems, as well as rainfed areas, were concentrated in certain villages. Care is needed in analysis to ensure the impact of irrigation is not confused with the impact of village-specific variables.

The average characteristics of household heads (Table 3) suggest few differences

Table 2. Distribution of farm area by irrigation facilities.[a]

Village	Av farm size (ha)	Irrigated area (ha)				
		Technical[b]	Semi-technical[c]	Simple[d]	Rainfed	Total
Pinrang						
Padakkalawa	0.99	1202	–	–	–	1202
Mattiro Deceng	0.77	1332	–	–	322	1654
Temmasarange	0.49	1286	–	–	59	1345
Matongang-tongang	1.96	1824	–	–	613	2437
Subtotal	1.22	5644	–	–	994	6638
Sidrap						
Rappang	1.03	209	–	–	–	209
Watang Sidenreng	1.79	2377	1658	–	37	4072
Lancirang	0.93	400	–	1819	250	2469
Tanru-Tedong	1.50	724	765	–	1119	2608
Subtotal	1.45	3710	2423	1819	1406	9358
Total	1.37	9354	2423	1819	2400	15996

[a]Source: Farm survey for farm sizes and village offices for irrigated area. [b]Irrigation infrastructure is complete, permitting control over water allocation through accurate measurement. [c]Irrigation infrastructure is incomplete, permitting some control over water allocation, but without accurate measurement. [d]Irrigation system is of simple construction, permitting little control over water allocation.

Table 3. Demographic characteristics by type of household.

Characteristic	Mechanized household	Nonmechanized household
No. of households	124	166
Av age of household head (yr)	39	40.4
Av education of household head (yr)	4.6	3.8
Av experience in farming (yr)	19.9	20.3
Av no. of household members	6.3	6.8
Av no. of permanent laborers	0.1	0.2

Source: Farm Survey, Mechanization Consequences, 1979.

between the mechanized and nonmechanized groups. By irrigation type, sharecropping appears to be most common on nonmechanized irrigated farms (Table 4). Owners accounted for over 50% of each of the other categories. Nonfarm income was far higher on the mechanized than on nonmechanized farms. One major limitation to mechanization was that there was only one village with a tractor repair shop. All other repair shops were in the towns.

EFFECTS OF MECHANIZATION

Intensity of land use

If lack of power is indeed a constraint to increasing cropping intensity, farmers adopting mechanized land preparation should increase cropping intensity. The record-keeping cooperators who used tractor custom services for land preparation were classified according to whether cropping intensity fell, remained constant, or increased following the adoption of minitractors (Table 5). The rainfed areas had some indication of an increase in cropping intensity; the irrigated area had none. Possible explanations include the relatively higher initial income of farmers in irrigated areas and the greater potential for increasing the cropping intensity of rainfed areas.

Comparing the area prepared by alternative power sources each week after water became available revealed that, in the wet season, farmers using draft animals completed land preparation quicker than those using minitractors. Farms using manual land preparation were last to complete the task, probably because of the absence of landless laborers. This situation is fairly similar to that in West Java and

Table 4. Economic characteristics of farmer cooperators.

Characteristic	Rainfed		Irrigated	
	Non-mechanized	Mechanized	Non-mechanized	Mechanized
Frequency of tenure type (%)				
Owner (75% or more)	74	58	35	49
Part owner (25-75%)	4	8	5	5
Sharecropper (25% or less owned)	22	31	60	45
Nonfarm income ($)	102	315	52	163
Farm implements ($)	40	40	45	29
Consumer durables ($)	123	173	99	102

Table 5. Change in cropping intensity associated with adoption of minitractor land preparation, by environment.

Environment	No.	Farmers (no.) indicating change in cropping intensity		
		Reduced	Same	Increased
Rainfed	18	2	11	5
Irrigated	26	1	25	0

the same explanations (widespread ownership of carabaos and rental of tractors) are probably valid.

Increased cropping intensity was not an important answer when farmers were asked reasons for purchasing or hiring minitractors for land preparation. The main reasons for purchasing minitractors were to plant on time (30%), improve the quality of land preparation (26%), increase yield (10%), and reduce drudgery (8%). For farmers who hired custom services, the main reasons were to improve the quality of land preparation (45%), plant on time (31%), increase yield (22%), and alleviate a labor shortage (13%).

A review of production practices in the area, shows that higher cropping intensities are possible. Achieving these may be facilitated by the use of tractors, but will also require the availability and promotion of complete input packages, including seeds, fertilizer, pesticides, credit, and technical information.

Labor use

Labor use data, by level of mechanization for the three seasons, are shown in Tables 6, 7, and 8. In the wet seasons nonmechanized farms employed about twice as much labor for land preparation as mechanized farms. Most of this was family labor. In the dry season, labor use for land preparation was almost the same. Labor use for crop establishment and maintenance, although varying by season, did not differ greatly within seasons between mechanized and nonmechanized farms.

For harvesting, all respondents hired laborers who used sickles. Labor use was largely a function of yield. Given that within the same water environment, mechanized farms used more fertilizer and obtained slightly higher yields. Labor use for harvesting was slightly higher on mechanized than on nonmechanized farms. However, this is unlikely to be an effect of mechanization.

When all of the components of labor use were aggregated, total labor use was

Table 6. Labor use for rice production, 1979 wet season.

Environment, operation	Nonmechanized labor (d/ha)			Mechanized labor (d/ha)		
	Family	Hired or exchange	Total	Family	Hired or exchange	Total
Rainfed						
Land preparation[a]	23.2	15.5	38.8	15.4	4.8	20.2
Establishment and maintenance	22.6	30.5	53.1	23.6	31.9	55.5
Harvest and transport	8.8	23.0	31.8	5.4	48.0	53.4
Others[b]	1.9	2.8	4.7	1.0	0.8	1.8
Total	56.6	71.8	128.4	45.4	85.1	130.9
Irrigated						
Land preparation[a]	25.0	4.2	29.2	7.8	3.8	11.6
Establishment and maintenance	21.8	25.5	47.3	15.6	23.3	38.9
Harvest and transport	2.3	20.0	22.3	2.0	47.8	49.8
Others[b]	5.0	0.0	5.0	2.8	0.4	3.2
Total	54.1	49.7	103.8	28.2	75.3	103.5

[a]Including seedbed preparation. [b]Irrigating and drying. Rainfed mechanized farms mostly sold at harvest without drying.

Table 7. Labor use for rice production, 1980 wet season.

Environment, operation	Nonmechanized labor (d/ha)			Mechanized labor (d/ha)		
	Family	Hired or exchange	Total	Family	Hired or exchange	Total
Rainfed						
Land preparation[a]	18.4	0.8	19.2	9.5	2.0	11.5
Establishment and maintenance	16.4	16.0	32.4	16.6	18.1	34.7
Harvest and transport	2.2	22.0	24.2	1.8	25.4	27.2
Others[b]	0.1	0.0	0.1	0.2	0.0	0.2
Total	37.1	38.8	75.9	28.1	45.5	73.6
Irrigated						
Land preparation[a]	20.4	1.1	21.5	7.6	4.1	11.7
Establishment and maintenance	14.4	18.3	32.7	13.6	16.1	29.7
Harvest and transport	0.9	26.7	27.6	1.4	28.5	29.9
Others[b]	0.9	0.0	0.9	1.5	0.0	1.5
Total	36.6	46.1	86.3	24.1	48.7	72.6

[a]Including seedbed preparation. [b]Irrigating and drying. Rainfed mechanized farms mostly sold at harvest without drying.

Table 8. Labor use for rice production, 1980-81 dry season.

Environment, operation	Nonmechanized labor (d/ha)			Mechanized labor (d/ha)		
	Family	Hired or exchange	Total	Family	Hired or exchange	Total
Rainfed						
Land preparation[a]	12.8	3.9	16.7	12.5	1.6	14.1
Establishment and maintenance	14.1	25.8	39.9	14.7	21.8	36.5
Harvest and transport	1.7	19.8	21.5	0.9	21.2	23.1
Others[b]	0.7	0.0	0.7	5.5	0.0	5.5
Total	29.3	49.5	78.8	33.6	46.1	79.2
Irrigated						
Land preparation[a]	14.5	1.1	15.6	8.7	2.8	11.5
Establishment and maintenance	11.4	20.8	32.2	13.1	17.7	30.8
Harvest and transport	0.9	31.3	32.2	0.9	31.3	32.2
Others[b]	0.6	0.0	0.6	1.3	0.0	1.3
Total	27.4	53.2	79.8	24.0	51.8	75.8

[a]Including seedbed preparation. [b]Irrigating and drying. Rainfed mechanized farms mostly sold at harvest without drying.

about the same on mechanized and nonmechanized farms, although its composition differed. Mechanized farms tended to use less family labor and to hire the same or more labor for certain operations. This action is likely to have positive social welfare implications.

Yield

Data on yields, fertilizer use, and crop failure by season for mechanized and nonmechanized farms are in Table 9. Yields per hectare planted, with a single exception, were higher on mechanized farms. After adjusting for crop failures, which affected the nonmechanized farms more, the differences in yield per hectare harvested were less pronounced. It was not investigated whether crop failure was reduced by mechanization.

Comparing the differences in total use of fertilizer and yields, the average minimum responses which would be required for fertilizer to account for the yield differences follow: for the rainfed farms, 6.2 kg yield/kg of fertilizer in the 1979 wet season, negative in the 1980 wet season, and 6.3 kg in the 1980-81 dry season; for the irrigated farms, 2.8 kg yield/kg of fertilizer in the 1979 wet season, 3.6 kg in the 1980 wet season, and negative in the 1980-81 dry season. It is reasonable to expect actual response to fertilizer to be higher than these values, and to conclude that mechanization has no positive impact on yields.

Table 9. Yield and fertilizer use per hectare of consequences cooperators.

| | Nonmechanized | | Mechanized | |
	Rainfed	Irrigated	Rainfed	Irrigated
	1979 wet season			
No. reporting	84	82	48	76
Fertilizer				
Urea (kg/ha)	45	45	84	136
Triple superphosphate (kg/ha)	1	5	3	52
Ammonium sulfate (kg/ha)	2	16	3	6
Total (kg/ha)	48	56	90	194
Yield (kg/planted ha)	508	1099	768	1551
Crop failure (%)	26	13	19	6
Yield (kg/harvested ha)	686	1263	948	1650
	1980 wet season			
No. reporting	71	30	40	83
Fertilizer				
Urea (kg/ha)	89	107	108	156
Triple superphosphate (kg/ha)	74	76	69	98
Ammonium sulfate (kg/ha)	31	46	58	70
Total (kg/ha)	194	229	235	324
Yield (kg/planted ha)	2552	2548	2413	2910
Crop failure (%)	–	3	–	2
Yield (kg/harvested ha)	2552	2627	2413	2969
	1980-81 dry season			
No. reporting	78	53	7	104
Fertilizer				
Urea (kg/ha)	103	77	130	152
Triple superphosphate (kg/ha)	33	61	74	59
Ammonium sulfate (kg/ha)	0	36	25	22
Total	136	174	229	233
Yield (kg/planted ha)	4214	5655	4841	4735
Crop failure (%)	1	2	0	0
Yield (kg/harvested ha)	4257	5770	4841	4735

CONCLUSIONS

The preliminary analyses of the South Sulawesi data suggest that mechanization on its own has no impact on cropping intensity in irrigated areas, but may have a positive impact in rainfed areas. However, benefits might be obtained if mechanization is included as part of a technology package. Similarly for yields, there is no evidence that mechanization results directly in increases.

Finally, mechanization appears to reduce the level of labor use, particularly family labor. Under these circumstances, mechanization is likely to result in increased social welfare because the labor displaced by machinery might find employment in other activities or more time for leisure and improving education levels. All these benefits are likely to assist national development.

REFERENCES CITED

Bernsten, R. H. 1981. Effects of minitractor mechanization on employment and labor use intensity, Sidrap and Pinrang, South Sulawesi, Indonesia. Consequences of Small Rice Farm Mechanization Project Working Paper 32. Los Baños, Laguna.

Maamun, Y. 1981. Site description: South Sulawesi. Consequences of Small Rice Farm Mechanization Project Working Paper 44. Los Baños, Laguna.

Maamun, Y., and D. Patong. 1978. The consequences of mechanization study in South Sulawesi, Indonesia (background information). IRRI Workshop, September.

Sarasutha, I.G.P., and R. Bernsten. 1981. Effect of mechanization on intensity of land use, South Sulawesi, Indonesia. Consequences of Small Rice Farm Mechanization Project Working Paper 45. Los Baños, Laguna.

Sinaga, R. 1981. Effects of mechanization on productivity: South Sulawesi, Indonesia. Consequences of Small Rice Farm Mechanization Project Working Paper 41. Los Baños, Laguna.

SSAC (South Sulawesi Agricultural Census). 1976.

SSAEO (South Sulawesi Agricultural Extension Office). 1978.